Short Plays

from the

GREAT CLASSICS

(for Young Actors and Actresses)

By VERNON HOWARD

with drawings by SHIZU

 STERLING PUBLISHING CO., Inc.   New York

MONOLOGUE AND PLAY BOOKS

By Vernon Howard

Acts for Comedy Shows
Getting Started as an Author
Holiday Monologues
Humorous Monologues
Monologues for Teens
More Charades & Pantomimes
Pantomimes, Charades and Skits
Puppet and Pantomime Plays
Short Plays from Great Classics
Talking to an Audience

Fourth Printing, 1966

Copyright © 1960 by
Sterling Publishing Co., Inc.
419 Park Avenue South, New York, N.Y. 10016
All rights reserved
Manufactured in the United States of America
Library of Congress Catalog Card No.: 60-10383

CONTENTS

HOW TO USE THIS BOOK

The 12 short plays in this book are all easy to stage, fun to act out and entertaining to watch. They are suitable for performing in a simple classroom or an elaborate auditorium, at a club meeting or a party at home. They may be used effectively during a Sunday school class or for a camp program, in front of a large audience or for just a few friends of the actors. Their main purpose is to entertain, and if they happen to instruct at the same time, that's just an added attraction.

NOTE TO THE TEACHER, LEADER OR COUNSELOR

Why these plays? The dramas here have been adapted from some of the best-loved classics of all time. Because actors and audience will probably be familiar with the original books, the plays will be especially attractive. The characters will seem like old friends given new life and the boys and girls who meet them again in dramatic form will feel closer identification with them as they participate in the action. If there are some members of the group who haven't yet read the books, the plays should arouse their interest and curiosity.

Each play is easy to put on. You need only a few props and little scenery. Preparation and rehearsal can be kept to a minimum and even the most inexperienced actor and actress can do a good job.

Select a play that seems best for your group. This book contains a wide variety of plays, so you can select those that especially appeal to you and your group. Go through the pages and choose those that are the most appropriate.

If you are an English teacher, you might put on a play when your class is reading the book from which it comes.

Some plays are shorter than others, and you should consider the amount of time you will have. Youngsters who have had some rehearsal will perform a play in less time than those who have not become very familiar with it. Yet each play is short enough to be performed during a class period or as part of an assembly program. Two or three classes or groups might prepare different scenes, and present one play after another to offer a complete show of an hour or so.

Some plays may be more appealing to girls; others to boys. There are roles for both boys and girls in most of the plays. If necessary, girls may play boys' roles, and vice versa. In some cases, the sex of characters is not specified, so you may cast whatever actors are available. Even if all the roles are to be taken by boys, the girls in your group will be an enthusiastic audience.

There are at least 10 roles in each play. Extras may be added or eliminated to meet casting requirements, but if your stage space is limited, you should not have an excessive number of extras.

Roles calling for players to appear as children should be filled by smaller performers, dressed according to the ages they represent.

Learning lines or reading? If time is limited, the actors may read their parts, as if they were performing for radio. This method is good when the performance is informal. Have the actors hold the book in one hand and gesture with the other. Reading will help them concentrate on gestures, facial expressions and tone of voice. They may become more confident of their dramatic abilities if they read the first play or two, and then go on to a full-scale performance. All first group rehearsals should be by reading aloud.

The stage. The stage may be as simple or as elaborate as your facilities permit. It may be just the front of a classroom, a section of a living room, a clearing at a camp or a real stage in an auditorium.

All stage directions are given from the viewpoint of the actors as they stand onstage and face the audience. This means that *left stage* is to the left of the actor, *right stage* is toward his own right. *Upstage* is toward the backdrop (real or imaginary); *downstage* is toward the audience. You can easily remember the difference between the two by picturing the stage as slanting downward toward the audience.

Actors should carefully follow the directions for entering or exiting from left or right wings (also real or imaginary), since they are usually significant to the action.

If you have no curtain, the stage may be set with characters and properties shortly before the audience is seated. Begin the action as soon as the Narrator exits.

Stage properties and sound effects. Basic ideas for properties and backgrounds are supplied. Those which play an important part in the action should be located according to directions. However, you may make changes or additions with details, using your imagination to create the effect you want. All items such as tools and weapons should be made from cardboard or some other soft and safe material.

Use offstage sound effects, if possible, for they add much to the dramatic impact. Two or three boys and girls could study the script and devise suitable and interesting sound effects. But do not overdo them, lest they distract the audience from the scene itself.

In some of the scenes, offstage music (from a record player) can help to put the audience into the proper emotional mood.

Costumes. Costumes may be simple or elaborate. Quite often a hat or coat will be enough to establish the character—a sailor's cap or crown or feathers, for example. The Narrator may appear in a costume representative of the period and country of the play. An old trunk will probably be full of wonderful costumes, and with a little ingenuity the cast can put together imaginative apparel.

NOTE TO THE ACTOR

Acting is fun! Whether your role is large or small, you have a great opportunity to discover and develop your dramatic talent and an excellent means for self-expression. Dramatics help you to build self-confidence, poise and leadership qualities. But let's get back to our first point—it's fun. You and your audience will enjoy and appreciate the entertainment provided by a play.

Consider the character that you will portray. Characterization is vital! First read the play through and take careful note of the character you will play. Notice at the same time the entrances and exits you will make, and the props you will use. Visualize how the character would say the lines, and if you are not going to read during the performance, learn your lines as quickly as possible. Then try to act as the person himself would act. For example, if you are portraying an old man, your movements should be somewhat slow and faltering. A young, bold man would be vigorous, decisive. Try to be the character, not yourself.

Rehearse your performance. Whether you are reading or learning your part, you'll feel more confident if you've had some rehearsal. Get off by yourself and say your lines several times. Pay special attention to the stage directions, and as you say the lines, smile or frown or do whatever is called for. You might practice in front of a mirror, watching your expressions and gestures. Try your part for your family or friends. They will probably

7

offer helpful hints. At all times, with or without an audience, speak clearly so every word can be understood. Don't mumble; don't speak too rapidly.

Remember that the art of dramatics requires a certain amount of exaggeration, but overplaying is as bad as underplaying. While *you* may know that your character is supposed to be happy or sad, you must make these emotions clear to the audience. Stress your gestures, your movements and your facial expressions so that they indicate a definite mood, but do not exaggerate them so much that they become unnatural and grotesque. It is often a good idea to exaggerate an emotion during rehearsal so that it becomes clearly fixed in your mind, and then tone it down during the performance.

When you rehearse with the rest of the cast, watch your timing. Observe the stage directions for pausing, turning, gesturing. Make sure that you enter and leave at just the right moment. Do not speak too soon nor too long after another actor has finished a line. If you have a real stage for your performance, start your walk onstage several steps back inside the wing. This gives you the appearance of coming from *somewhere*, and not merely from offstage. Be sure the audience cannot see you while you are waiting for your cue to enter.

Remember that the more familiar you become with your role, the easier and more natural it will be. Finally, remain relaxed, confident, alert—and you will give a performance that will be pleasing to you and entertaining to your audience.

Now, CURTAIN UP. The play is about to begin . . . .

THE TREASURE OF MONTE CRISTO

CHARACTERS

Narrator
Jacopo
Edmond Dantes
The Captain
First Sailor
Second Sailor

Third Sailor
Fourth Sailor
Fifth Sailor
Sixth Sailor
Seventh Sailor
Extra Sailors

INTRODUCTION BY NARRATOR

Ladies and gentlemen, welcome to this evening's performance. Tonight we present a scene from one of the most exciting adventure stories ever written. Our play is entitled "The Treasure of Monte Cristo." It is adapted from the classic story *The Count of Monte Cristo*, written by the French author, Alexandre Dumas.

Let us briefly review the events leading up to tonight's scene. Our hero is Edmond Dantes, a young sailor who was arrested and imprisoned on false charges brought against him by French officials. Edmond was sent to the Chateau d'If, a prison located on an island in the Mediterranean Sea. While at the Chateau d'If he found himself in a cell next to another innocent prisoner —a kindly old clergyman. The clergyman told Edmond of a fabulous treasure which was buried on the isle of Monte Cristo

—a treasure that would be Edmond's if he could manage to escape.

After fourteen years in prison, Dantes *did* escape. He did this by sewing himself into a large sack which was tossed into the sea by his unsuspecting jailers. After several miserable hours in the cold water he was picked up by a shipload of smugglers. The captain called Edmond by the name of *Maltese* . . . and invited him to become one of the crew.

One day the captain decided to make camp on the deserted isle of Monte Cristo—the very place where the secret treasure was buried in a cave. As they landed, Dantes wondered if he could find the treasure without arousing the suspicions of the crew. Our story opens as Dantes and the smugglers make camp on the treasure island of Monte Cristo. (*Narrator exits. Curtain rises.*)

SETTING AT RISE OF CURTAIN

The scene is a campsite near the shore. Nautical and general equipment, such as chests, crates and telescopes, along with a pile of sticks (representing rifles) are set in the background. A burned-out campfire is at stage center.

Jacopo, a sailor, sits at the fire and idly pokes at the ashes with a stick. He looks up as Dantes enters from right.

JACOPO (*in friendly greeting*): Ah, my Maltese friend, where have you been? Ever since landing you have been poking around the coastline. What do you expect to find in this dreary place?

DANTES (*shrugging, warming his hands over the fire*): Monte Cristo is a strange island. Who knows what I may stumble across? (*Glancing around.*) Where are the others?

JACOPO (*gesturing*): On shipboard, going over the charts. The captain is planning a new voyage. (*Grinning.*) Even smugglers must find new and profitable sources of plunder. (*He reaches into a nearby box, taking some bread.*) Sit awhile and share some bread and cheese.

DANTES (*taking a "rifle"*): Later, Jacopo. I want to explore the east coast.

JACOPO (*protesting*): But you've just come back. In and out, up and down. (*Gesturing.*) What's out there, anyway? (*Sighing, rising.*) Ah, well . . . maybe I can help you. Let's be off.

DANTES (*shaking head*): No, no; I prefer to go alone. You're such a clumsy fellow; you're liable to go lame on me. Stay here and keep us a warm fire.

JACOPO (*shrugging, sitting*): At least fetch us back a fresh goat for dinner. (*Breaking bread, scowling at it.*) The foul weather makes mold of our bread.

(*As Dantes starts to leave toward right, the Captain and the first six Sailors plus Extra Sailors, enter from left. They stand or sit around the fire.*)

FIRST SAILOR (*to Dantes, gruffly*): Hold on, Maltese sailorman. We've had enough of your wanderings. Get back here. (*To others, sarcastically, as he gestures toward Dantes.*) Here is a curious fellow. He would rather tramp around this bleak rock than make his fortune with us. (*Commanding Dantes.*) Get over here and explain a few things about yourself.

CAPTAIN (*to First Sailor, sternly*): I'm still captain of this crew, Mister Watkins; and I'll give the orders. (*To Dantes, briskly but kindly.*) Why not spill yourself to us? Who knows?— maybe we can help.

SECOND SAILOR (*to Dantes who returns to fire*): You tell us that you are a seaman—and you are for sure. You skip the deck as spryly as any of us. But about your past we know nothing!

CAPTAIN (*to Dantes*): Do you know the Mediterranean?

DANTES: I've sailed it since boyhood.

CAPTAIN: You know the best ports?

DANTES: I could enter most of them blindfolded.

CAPTAIN (*watching Dantes closely*): And your last port of call . . . where was it?

DANTES: With all respect, Captain, I'll keep that to myself.

CAPTAIN (*chuckling*): You're not easily tricked, shipmate. We can use your sharp wits.

THIRD SAILOR (*to Dantes*): There is usually a woman mixed up in a man's secrets. (*Gesturing.*) Tell us, do you have a lady hidden out there in the caves? (*Crew chuckles.*)

DANTES (*nodding with good humor*): There is a lady . . . (*Soberly.*) A lovely lady named Mercedes . . . whom I haven't seen for fourteen years.

FOURTH SAILOR (*laughing*): Maybe our mysterious shipmate is a member of royalty. (*Bowing mockingly to Dantes.*) Hail to the count of Monte Cristo . . . or is it duke? Perhaps Napoleon Bonaparte himself! (*Others laugh good-naturedly.*)

FIFTH SAILOR (*jokingly*): No, shipmates; our Maltese friend is an agent of the French government. His specialty is smugglers. (*Grinning, holding out wrists to Dantes.*) I confess! Haul me away! Ha!

SIXTH SAILOR (*sarcastically eyeing Dantes*): I suspect the joke may be on us. I've been watching this sly mate of ours. He's keeping something from us . . . and I intend to find it out. (*The crew sobers somewhat.*)

CAPTAIN (*reproving Sixth Sailor*): You and your suspicious mind. (*To Dantes.*) Speak for yourself, Maltese. Answer these rascals.

DANTES (*boldly, confidently*): Keeping things from you?—of course I am—just as you guard your own secrets. You are wanted by the Paris police? (*Shrugging.*) That is your own business. You owe a pile of debts to fifteen merchants in fifteen ports? That is your affair, not mine. Do I pry into your life? Not at all. And neither will I permit you to force my secrets. (*Gesturing.*) Fair enough, shipmates?

JACOPO (*applauding and grinning*): Well spoken! (*Glancing at others.*) We are desperate sea-dogs at that. One step from pirates, every man of us.

CAPTAIN (*briskly businesslike*): Enough of this. We've got plans to make. (*To First Sailor*). Fetch the chart. (*As First Sailor obeys, Dantes takes a rifle.*)

DANTES (*gesturing*): I spotted a herd of goats on the far side. We'll have a roast joint for dinner.

FIRST SAILOR (*to others, suspiciously*): See what I mean? (*Sourly.*) I suspect he has more than a roast joint on his mind.

CAPTAIN (*shooing Dantes away*): Fresh meat—there's a tasty idea. Off with you.

JACOPO (*to Dantes who walks towards right wing*): Take care . . . the shore rocks are slippery. We want you back safely with our dinner. (*Dantes exits. All except First Sailor bend over the chart and talk in low tones. The First Sailor walks suspiciously toward right, pauses briefly while peering at the departing Dantes, finally follows him offstage.*)

CAPTAIN (*gesturing to crates*): Now . . . we have stocks of Turkish rugs . . . chests of fine spices from the Orient. We need ideas for selling them. Where can we get the best price for our plunder?

SECOND SAILOR (*growling*): The coast of France gets more dangerous by the hour. No matter where we try to get ashore we are likely to be greeted by the police. I'm for hiding out right here for a few days.

THIRD SAILOR (*protesting*): While our hard-earned loot spoils by the sea? (*Scowling.*) The weather is foul enough to eat the steel off our knives. Let's get away—take our chances.

FOURTH SAILOR (*glumly*): A smuggler's lot is a miserable one at that. I'm for abandoning the whole mess and turning into an honest man. (*Sighing.*) Ah, for the peaceful life with a quiet home and a loving wife. I think, shipmates, you have seen the last of me on board.

SEVENTH SAILOR (*entering from left with armful of clothing, glancing around*): Where is our new shipmate? I've brought him extra clothing. Those rags he wore when we fished him from the sea . . . fah! . . . not fit for a beggar.

SIXTH SAILOR (*suddenly, sourly, as he glares toward right wing*): I'm getting more suspicious by the minute. (*To Captain.*) Captain, think it over. After we pulled him from the water we heard a roar of cannon from the prison of Chateau d'If. That gun is fired only when there is an escape.

JACOPO (*shrugging, gesturing nonchalantly*): So he is wanted at the prison. (*To Sixth Sailor, sarcastically.*) How many jails want you, my innocent shipmate? (*Others roar with laughter.*)

SIXTH SAILOR (*angrily*): But that's not my point. Why does he make mystery of the Chateau d'If?

FIRST SAILOR (*entering from right, scowling*): Gave me the slip, he did. He's hunting all right. . . . (*Nodding knowingly.*) But not for goatmeat.

CAPTAIN (*somewhat annoyed*): We spend too much time talking about him. We have enough problems of our own.

JACOPO (*glancing over his shoulder, towards right wing*): We should have heard from his rifle by now. I warned him of treacherous rocks. (*Rising.*) I'll have a look. (*Jacopo exits at right.*)

SIXTH SAILOR (*forcefully*): I tell you, shipmates, there's something up. I've heard of buried treasure on Monte Cristo. Maybe that's his game.

SEVENTH SAILOR (*to Sixth Sailor, scoffing*): There's not a spot in the seven seas without its treasure tales. You show more greed than good sense.

FIFTH SAILOR (*staring toward right wing, leaping up*): He's hurt! (*Fifth Sailor races offstage at right, returns while helping Jacopo to support the injured Dantes. They place him near the fire as the others gather around.*)

SECOND SAILOR: What happened?

DANTES (*gasping painfully*): Inside a sea cave . . . lost my footing . . . fell on sharp stones. (*Adjusting his position.*) There now . . . let me be . . . I'll mend fast enough.

FIRST SAILOR (*to Dantes, suspiciously, sarcastically*): What kind of goat hangs around the sea caves?

SIXTH SAILOR (*peering suspiciously*): What do you say to that?

CAPTAIN: (*gruffly*) Hold your tongues—the man is in pain enough. (*To Dantes.*) I've decided to set sail at once, before the weather ruins our prizes. If we wait until evening, you'll be in shape for moving aboard. All right, shipmate?

DANTES (*protesting*): No, Captain, don't wait on my account. Leave me with some biscuits and water—perhaps a pickax to defend myself.

FIRST SAILOR (*mockingly*): Or perhaps to dig with?

THIRD SAILOR: No, Maltese, we'll not abandon you. Smugglers we may be, but we're loyal to our comrades.

DANTES (*shaking head*): I'll be all right. Just send a ship for me as soon as you can. (*Shifting painfully*). In a day or two I'll be able to move these aching bones.

JACOPO: There's just one way to settle things. (*Pointing to himself.*) I will stay with him. The rest of you rascals go and bring us a rich profit for our goods.

DANTES (*to Jacopo*): You have a kind heart, Jacopo, but there's no need. I'm used to hardship, I assure you.

CAPTAIN (*to Dantes*): Have no worry. We'll send a ship for you within the week. (*To Sailors, authoritatively.*) Load the crates! We're off for the coast of France!

(*The action divides as follows: Jacopo sets small boxes of equipment next to Dantes; they chat in low tones. All Sailors—except the First and the Sixth—pick up equipment and exit at left. The First and Sixth Sailors sneak aside to upstage left, whispering furtively.*)

FIRST SAILOR (*calling, beckoning*): Captain!

CAPTAIN (*approaching briskly*): Yes, what is it?

SIXTH SAILOR (*grasping Captain's arm, frowning towards Dantes*): What man in his right mind would insist on staying here alone? (*Fiercely.*) I'm for forcing his secret from him right here and now.

FIRST SAILOR (*greedily*): He may have a secret worth ten times our Turkish rugs.

CAPTAIN (*angrily jerking away*): You'd stab your own shipmate in the back? You're the worst scoundrels in the lot. (*Gesturing toward left.*) Get on board! (*Captain exits at left.*)

SIXTH SAILOR (*shaking his fist after the departing Captain*): The Captain's a bungler. (*Eagerly.*) Here's our plan. (*Gesturing towards upstage right.*) We'll hide out in the hills where we can watch the Maltese. Make no mistake, as soon as the ship sails he'll be up to something.

FIRST SAILOR (*greedily rubbing hands*): And whatever he finds we'll grab for ourselves!

SIXTH SAILOR (*laughing sarcastically*): When we are through with him he'll have no use for gold or anything else. Let's go! (*As they start to cross to right wing the Captain enters from left, curtly hails them.*)

CAPTAIN: Misters!

FIRST SAILOR (*viciously, as both Sailors halt and turn*): I warn you, Captain, stay out of this.

CAPTAIN (*grimly*): And I warn you, gentlemen. If you as much as touch the Maltese I'll have your hides. Understand me, misters. Now get on board. (*The Captain glares at them for a moment, exits at left.*)

SIXTH SAILOR (*as both scowl and hesitate*): Fah! It's not worth the risk. We'd better go along with the ship. (*They glumly exit at left.*)

JACOPO (*making final comforts for Dantes*): Take good care of yourself, Maltese. I need a friend like you.

DANTES (*nodding*): I need you, too, Jacopo. I'll not forget your kindnesses when we meet again.

JACOPO (*stepping back, grinning*): Just one thing . . . all this talk about buried treasure . . . I wonder if you really do have your secret. (*Waving cheerfully.*) Ah, well, that is still your affair. Good fortune, shipmate.

DANTES: Good-by, Jacopo. (*Dantes watches Jacopo who exits at left. With difficulty, Dantes raises himself to his feet, picks up cardboard pickax, leans against a crate. Looking seaward— toward audience—he shades his eyes with his palm. He speaks slowly as he watches the ship sail away.*) Good-by, friends . . . my griefs of the past sail with you. My future is in my own hands at last. (*Lowering palm, nodding, still looking seaward.*) Yes, ship-mates, there is a rich treasure on Monte Cristo . . . and I shall find it. (*Turning, gesturing into right wing.*) It's out there some-where . . . waiting for me. (*He walks with difficulty toward right.*) Then for France again . . . and Mercedes . . . and a new life. (*He exits at right. Curtain descends.*)

®liver Twist Asks for More

CHARACTERS

Narrator	Mr. Bumble
Oliver Twist	Mr. Limbkins
First Boy	Mr. Gamfield
Second Boy	First Magistrate
Third Boy	Second Magistrate
Cook	Extra Boys
Maid	

INTRODUCTION BY NARRATOR

Ladies and gentlemen, welcome to this evening's performance. Our play is called "Oliver Twist Asks For More." No doubt you recognize that our story is based on the classic book *Oliver Twist*, written by that famous English author, Charles Dickens.

You may recall that Oliver was an orphan boy who was lonely, frightened and hungry . . . especially *hungry*.

Our play takes place at a workhouse for homeless boys. Oliver and his friends have just finished their supper—that is, if you can call a small bowl of oatmeal a supper. (*Narrator exits. Curtain rises.*)

SETTING AT RISE OF CURTAIN

Oliver and the three other poorly-dressed boys, plus Extra Boys, are seated behind a long, plain table. The room is bare and cheerless.

The boys hungrily scrape the last bit of oatmeal from their bowls, then set them down while sighing.

FIRST BOY (*painfully*): I'm still hungry.

SECOND BOY (*licking spoon*): We are always still hungry. Not even a crust of bread tonight.

THIRD BOY (*to Oliver*): Don't forget your promise, Oliver. (*As the Cook enters from right, the Third Boy nudges Oliver, whispers.*) There he is. Go ahead. (*Oliver timidly hesitates as the Cook approaches table. The Cook snatches two or three bowls, grabs Oliver's.*)

COOK (*gruffly, sourly*): Get back to your work. No time for idleness around here.

OLIVER (*holding out hand*): Please, sir, may I have my bowl back? There's a spoonful left. . . .

COOK (*slamming bowl on table*): Finish and be off with you! (*The Cook turns away to collect other bowls.*)

FIRST BOY (*whispering anxiously to Oliver*): Hurry!

OLIVER (*rising, choking with fright as he speaks to Cook*): Please, sir. . . .

COOK (*sourly*): What do you want? Speak up, boy.

OLIVER (*miserably shaking head, sitting down*): Nothing . . . nothing, sir. (*The Cook growls and busies himself at a far end of the table. The boys turn hopefully toward Oliver.*)

SECOND BOY (*pleading with Oliver*): Oliver, please . . . you promised to ask for more supper. (*Oliver nervously fingers his bowl and spoon, finally picks them up, rises and circles to stand in back of the Cook.*)

OLIVER (*stammering*): Sir . . . could you please. . . .

COOK (*turning around, scowling, nodding, reaching for Oliver's bowl*): Through at last? All right, I'll take your bowl.

OLIVER (*holding bowl up with both hands*): Please, sir, I want some more. (*The stunned Cook is speechless for a moment. He claps a hand to his forehead.*)

COOK (*exploding*): What! What did you say?

OLIVER (*trembling*): Please, sir, I want some more supper.

COOK (*staring in horror at Oliver*): What! What's that? You have the nerve to stand there and demand more supper? Why, you ungrateful wretch! More indeed! I'll teach you! (*He swings at Oliver who dodges. The Cook whirls, screams into left wing.*) Mr. Bumble! Mr. Limbkins! We are betrayed! Treachery under our very noses! (*Mr. Bumble and Mr. Limbkins, two harsh, self-righteous characters, race in from left, glance around in alarm.*)

MR. BUMBLE (*excitedly*): What's happened?

MR. LIMBKINS (*anxiously*): Are we on fire? (*The Cook takes Oliver by the ear and leads him before the two men. Oliver cringes.*)

COOK (*slowly, emphasizing his words*): This boy . . . this miserable, wretched, ungrateful scoundrel has dared to push his empty bowl into my face. (*Shouting.*) He asked for more supper!

MR. BUMBLE (*horrified*): For more supper? Unbelievable!

MR. LIMBKINS (*gasping*): After all we have done for him! I am painfully shocked! (*Shaking Oliver.*) Young man, you are the worst of scoundrels! What evil within your heart rebels against our kindness?

OLIVER (*trembling*): I . . . I am not ungrateful for your many kindnesses, sir . . . but . . . I am still hungry. (*Gesturing to boys.*) We thought your generosity might spare another mouthful to fill our emptiness.

MR. LIMBKINS (*arrogantly*): Tell me, boy, how hungry would you be if we put you out on the streets where you belong? (*Painfully grimacing.*) How it grieves my kindly heart to witness such rash impudence.

MR. BUMBLE (*leering*): Perhaps a few days in a dark cellar will cleanse him of evil. (*Pompously nodding.*) Yes, yes, for the boy's own good we must punish him severely. (*He nods self-righteously in unison with Mr. Limbkins.*)

MR. LIMBKINS (*to Oliver, with dramatic hypocrisy*): How fortunate for your soul's welfare to find yourself in such merciful hands as ours. (*The two men again nod in solemn unison as Oliver backs away.*)

MAID (*entering from left*): Mr. Limbkins, sir, there is a Mr. Gamfield at the door. He wishes to hire an apprentice chimney sweep.

MR. LIMBKINS (*whispering brightly to Mr. Bumble*): Hear that? A heaven-sent opportunity to get rid of a certain trouble-maker. (*Greedily rubbing palms together.*) Think of the money we'll save. (*To Maid.*) Show him in. (*The Maid curtsies and exits as the two men greedily leer at each other.*)

COOK (*shouting to boys*): Clear the table! Get on with the kitchen-work! (*The boys clear the table and start to exit at right.*)

MR. BUMBLE (*calling sharply to Oliver*): Oliver Twist! (*Jabbing a finger toward floor.*) Come here! (*Oliver hands his bowl to another boy as the boys and the Cook exit at right.*)

OLIVER (*timidly approaching*): Yes, Mr. Bumble?

MR. BUMBLE (*pompously*): Oliver, my lad, you shall see that our mercy is equal to our justice.

OLIVER (*bewildered*): I don't understand.

MR. LIMBKINS: Mr. Gamfield needs a strong, healthy boy to serve as an apprentice chimney sweep. You shall be a man of business! What do you say to that?

OLIVER (*gratefully*): Oh, sir, you are a kindly gentleman. (*Timidly asking.*) You have forgiven my rashness in asking for more supper?

MR. BUMBLE (*with false loftiness*): Our humble hearts are always ready to forgive a repentant sinner. (*Gesturing toward right.*) Go, put yourself into a clean shirt; prepare yourself for Mr. Gamfield.

OLIVER: Thank you, sir. (*As he exits at right, Mr. Gamfield stomps in from left.*)

MR. GAMFIELD (*snarling, shaking a fist at the two men*): Mind you, none of your usual tricks. I want a lad who'll give me a full day's work with little supper to show for it. (*Suddenly whining, hunching.*) I am a poor, poor man with scarcely a coat on my back.

MR. LIMBKINS (*eager to please*): Yes, of course. I'm sure you'll be pleased with our selection. (*Scowling toward right wing.*) Where is that boy? (*Shouting.*) Oliver! Oliver Twist! (*Oliver races onstage.*)

OLIVER: Sorry I took so long, sir.

MR. BUMBLE (*to Oliver, gesturing expansively*): Oliver, my boy, meet Mr. Gamfield, a generous soul whose heart bursts with love for all mankind. (*Sternly.*) You do want to go with him, don't you?

OLIVER (*timidly, hesitantly*): I . . . I guess so.

MR. GAMFIELD (*roughly feeling Oliver's arm*): Humph! A scrawny lad. (*Sourly.*) I have no intention of feeding his hungry muscles from my poor, poor kitchen.

MR. LIMBKINS: Come, come, the boy is a prize package indeed! All he needs is a whack across the back now and then. (*Hypocritically.*) For his own good, of course.

MR. GAMFIELD (*viciously leering at Oliver*): There'll be plenty of whacks if you turn out to be a stubborn donkey. (*Nodding, grumbling.*) We have a bargain. Get the boy's papers.

OLIVER (*pleading*): Please, Mr. Limbkins, may I ask. . . .

MR. LIMBKINS (*roaring*): Silence, you rude rascal! Off to the corner with you! (*Sighing, as Oliver retreats to upstage right.*) I'm afraid, sir, you'll have to whip some manners into him. (*Briskly rubbing his palms together.*) One moment, gentlemen, while I fetch the legal papers. (*As he starts to leave toward left, the Maid appears at left.*)

MAID: Sir, the magistrates are here.

MR. LIMBKINS (*angrily shocked*): The magistrates! (*Sourly.*) Those busybodies.

MR. GAMFIELD (*Puzzledly*): What do they want?

MR. BUMBLE (*scowling*): They are the law. No boy can leave here without their approval.

MR. LIMBKINS (*to Maid, in nervous confusion*): Uh . . . hold off those worthy gentlemen for a moment. (*The Maid curtsies and exits. Mr. Limbkins angrily beckons to Oliver who races over to the three stern men.*) Mind your manners, Mr. Oliver Twist, or you'll regret it.

MR. BUMBLE (*wagging a finger close to Oliver*): If they ask if you want to go with Mr. Gamfield you had better say yes.

OLIVER (*timidly protesting*): But, sir . . . (*Mr. Bumble misses a slap at Oliver as the two Magistrates enter from left, carrying legal papers. The Magistrates are elderly, kind and simple characters. The First Magistrate is so nearsighted that he blinks constantly. The Maid enters behind them, crosses stage to exit at right.*)

MR. LIMBKINS (*fawning, as the three men assume exaggerated airs of charm and friendliness*): Ah, honored gentlemen! What brings you to us today?

FIRST MAGISTRATE: We heard that Mr. Gamfield was seeking an apprentice. We wish to examine the boy.

MR. BUMBLE (*eager to impress*): Of course, of course. First and foremost we wish for the lad's happiness and welfare. (*Calling loudly but courteously into right wing.*) Young gentlemen, please bring table and chairs. Also pen and ink. Hurry, please, we mustn't keep our guests waiting. (*Four or five boys carry a small table and two chairs to center stage in front of the dining table. As they leave, Mr. Bumble assumes a broad smile and gestures in friendly fashion after them.*) Thank you for your kindly cooperation. (*To Magistrates, fawning.*) Notice the kindness and affection we extend to our young friends. (*He sighs hypocritically.*)

MR. LIMBKINS: Please be seated, sirs. (*As the Magistrates sit, Mr. Limbkins prods Oliver who steps before the table. The three men stand menacingly behind Oliver. The First Magistrate fumbles with his papers for a moment, finally looks up at Oliver.*)

FIRST MAGISTRATE (*smiling*): So you are the young man who wishes to become a chimney sweep. What is your name?

OLIVER: Oliver Twist, sir.

SECOND MAGISTRATE: Oliver Twist. Hmmmm . . . that's an interesting name.

OLIVER: The orphanage gave us names according to the alphabet. When I arrived they used the letter T.

FIRST MAGISTRATE: Would you like to be apprenticed to Mr. Gamfield? Hmmmm . . . (*As both Magistrates peer down at papers, Mr. Bumble shakes Oliver's arm, urging him to reply.*)

OLIVER (*hesitantly*): I . . . I . . . suppose so.

MR. GAMFIELD (*trying to explain*): As you can plainly see, the boy is so overwhelmed with gratitude that he can hardly speak. (*Pinching Oliver.*) Isn't that right, my boy? (*Oliver remains miserably silent.*)

SECOND MAGISTRATE (*to Mr. Gamfield*): I trust you will take good care of him?

MR. GAMFIELD (*laying a hand on Oliver's shoulders, groaning with a false air of compassion*): Care of him, indeed! Like a sparrow cares for a birdling! (*Oliver tearfully sniffs. He unsuccessfully tries to control himself as he is jabbed by one of the men.*)

FIRST MAGISTRATE (*nodding as he fumbles for and takes the pen*): Well, then, I believe we can happily settle the boy's future. I'll sign him over to you, Mr. Gamfield. Hmmmm . . . where is that inkwell? (*He blinks, peers around for the inkwell but fails to find it because it is directly under his nose. In the course of his peering he chances to look up at the quietly weeping Oliver. He sets the pen down, peers with kindly curiosity at Oliver. Note: This is climactic action which should be clearly performed. The First*

Magistrate speaks to Oliver.) My boy, you look pale and alarmed.

MR. GAMFIELD (*desperately trying to explain*): It's nothing at all, I assure you. So eager is he to go with me that he weeps with joy! (*Mr. Gamfield is so angry that his next jab at Oliver is clumsily obvious.*)

SECOND MAGISTRATE (*to the three men, sharply*): Stand back— all of you! (*To Oliver, gently.*) Now, boy, tell us what's the matter. Don't be afraid.

OLIVER (*bursting forth with sobs, pleading desperately to Mr. Limbkins*): Please sir—starve me, beat me, chain me in the cellar; do anything but please don't send me away with this cruel man.

MR. LIMBKINS (*indignantly throwing up arms, groaning painfully*): Oh, the cunning deceit of his young lips! (*To Magistrates, sorrowfully.*) I'm afraid his worthless character is exposed at last. (*Clicking tongue, bowing head.*) Tch, tch, tch. We must double our prayers for his poor misguided soul.,

FIRST MAGISTRATE (*somewhat sarcastically*): A touching performance, sir. (*Rising, speaking gently to Oliver.*) Oliver, my decision is made. You need not go with Mr. Gamfield.

OLIVER (*gratefully relieved*): Thank you, thank you. (*To Mr. Limbkins, anxiously*). Mr. Limbkins, I hope I haven't offended you. Please, sir, I'm sorry. (*Mr. Limbkins glares furiously at Oliver.*)

SECOND MAGISTRATE (*soberly and sternly*): Gentlemen, we warn you against whipping this boy. Treat him kindly, for we shall be watching you.

MR. BUMBLE (*nervously, in fear*): Yes, sir, sorry, sir. You shall be watching us. (*The Magistrates go around the table to Oliver.*)

FIRST MAGISTRATE (*patting the sniffing Oliver on head*): There, there, young Mr. Twist. We shall find a suitable place for you, How would you like to ship out to sea? Or perhaps we can find a place for you in the countryside? Good-by. (*To the men, sternly.*) Good-day, gentlemen. I trust you won't forget our warning. (*As the Magistrates exit at left, the three men angrily surround the fearfully cowering Oliver.*)

MR. GAMFIELD (*starting to take off his coat, speaking fiercely to Oliver*): Now for you, my lad.

MR. BUMBLE (*gesturing with terror toward left wing*): No, no! They'll find out! (*Scowling in defeat at Oliver.*) Bah! He's not worth the beating. (*Mr. Bumble sourly stalks out at left.*)

MR. GAMFIELD (*snarling at Oliver*): At least I won't have to feed the rascal. (*Muttering as he stomps toward left.*) Probably eats like a young horse. (*He exits at left while growling.*)

MR. LIMBKINS (*wringing his hands in despair*): I am ordered to treat him with kindness! (*Weeping.*) How can a cruel creature like me treat anyone with kindness? (*Shrugging, sighing.*) Ah, well, perhaps I can learn. (*Dismally shaking his head, he exits at left. Immediately, the boys race in from right.*)

THIRD BOY (*clapping Oliver on back*): We heard everything! Oliver, you're saved!

FIRST BOY (*nodding*): It's a good thing that old gentleman looked up in time and saw you.

OLIVER (*eagerly*): Did you hear what he said? Maybe we can all ship out to sea!

MAID (*entering from right, shoving the reluctant Cook before her*): Which one of you boys asked for more supper?

SECOND BOY (*as boys turn toward Oliver*): Our brave friend, Oliver Twist!

MAID (*to Oliver*): The cook has something to say to you (*Prodding the cook.*) Speak up!

COOK (*gruffly but not unkindly*): I've found a bit more supper in the kitchen. (*Grinning.*) For everyone. (*The boys cheer.*)

THIRD BOY (*to Oliver*): Lead the way, Oliver! And thanks for asking for more! (*The boys crowd around Oliver as all exit at right. Curtain falls.*)

JOHNNY APPLESEED
IN DANGER

CHARACTERS

Narrator

Johnny Appleseed

First Child

Second Child

Third Child

First Mother

Second Mother

Third Mother

First Indian

Second Indian

Third Indian

Fourth Indian

Extra Children and

Indians

INTRODUCTION BY NARRATOR

Welcome to our theatre, ladies and gentlemen. Tonight we present for your enjoyment a short play entitled "Johnny Appleseed in Danger." It is adapted from the life and legend of a person who actually lived, for Johnny Appleseed was more than just the hero of a folk tale. His real name was John Chapman, and he lived during the pioneer days of America when there were log cabins, oxcarts, and savage Indian tribes.

When our play begins, Johnny Appleseed has been wandering through the wilderness for many, many years, stopping for short visits in Ohio, Indiana and Illinois. Perhaps some of you wonder why he wandered around so much. And maybe you'd like to know what he did when he visited a new section of the country. Our play will now answer your questions. (*Narrator exits. Curtain rises.*)

SETTING AT RISE OF CURTAIN

Bushes, flowers and other plant life are set around the stage background. The rest of the stage is bare.

The three children, plus Extras if desired, are playing about, racing and shouting.

FIRST CHILD (*shouting to Second Child*): You can't catch me!

SECOND CHILD: I can, too! (*Second Child chases First Child around stage until they reach left stage. They suddenly halt, peer curiously into left wing.*) Wait a minute! Who's that coming? (*All children stop playing to peer toward left.*)

THIRD CHILD: It's a funny old fellow with a sack over his shoulder. I wonder who he is.

FIRST CHILD: Let's hide back here! (*The children scramble behind the bushes at upstage right.*

As they watch, Johnny slowly enters from left. He is elderly, bearded, barefoot, and simply dressed. He wears an old hat and carries a sack over his shoulder. He looks around, sets the sack on floor, goes through motions of scooping a small hole in the ground. He takes a seed—imaginary—from sack and goes through motions of planting and covering it. He wanders around left stage, selects another spot, plants a second seed.)

SECOND CHILD (*curiously, in stage whisper*): What's he doing? (*Straining to see.*) What's in his sack? (*Johnny plants a third seed, wanders offstage at left while searching for another planting area.*)

THIRD CHILD (*straining to see Johnny*): There he goes again!

FIRST MOTHER (*entering from right with other mothers, glancing anxiously around, calling*): Sarah, where are you? Children, come here!

FIRST CHILD (*as children step out*): Here we are. (*Excitedly gesturing toward left wing.*) We're watching that old man over there. Do you know who he is?

FIRST MOTHER (*barely glancing at Johnny, grabbing First Child's hand*): Never mind that for now—it's not safe out here.

29

(*The mothers quickly herd the children toward right stage; the children hang back.*)

SECOND CHILD (*to mothers*): What's the matter? (*Glancing toward Johnny.*) Is he a dangerous man?

SECOND MOTHER (*shaking head*): No, it's not that. We've just heard that unfriendly Indians are around. Hurry!

THIRD MOTHER (*to mothers, as she gestures toward the still-offstage Johnny*): We ought to warn him. (*Calling to Johnny.*) Sir! There are Indians lurking about ... you'd better get back to the village. (*Frowning, shaking head.*) He didn't hear me. We should make sure he understands. (*All players hurry toward left.*) Sir! You're in danger. Come with us.

(*While they are turned toward left, three Indians, with Extras if desired, enter from right, carrying cardboard tomahawks and bows and arrows. They stand at right stage, blocking the way, fiercely scowling. The others turn around to exit at right, suddenly see Indians. The mothers gasp and grab the children. All react in fright.*)

FIRST INDIAN (*accusingly*): You settlers have taken our lands and rivers; you have driven us from our homes. (*Stepping forward.*) We will take revenge.

FIRST MOTHER: Please, let us return to our village.

SECOND MOTHER: We mean you no harm.

SECOND INDIAN (*angrily*): Your soldiers have already done us great evil. (*Gesturing toward sky.*) Every moon we have less and less food for our women and children.

THIRD MOTHER: If you will return with us to our village we will give you food for your families.

THIRD INDIAN (*fiercely*): No! We will hunt our own food on our own lands. We will drive you from our hills and rivers.

(*As the Indians slowly and fiercely approach, Johnny enters from left. As he grasps the situation, he steps between the Indians and the settlers.*)

JOHNNY APPLESEED (*courageously, to Indians*): Stand where you are!

FIRST INDIAN (*scoffing, as he studies Johnny*): Ha! Where is your rifle, old man? All settlers carry rifles to hunt us down.

JOHNNY APPLESEED (*soberly shaking head*): I carry neither rifle nor hunting knife. I am a friend of your people.

SECOND INDIAN (*suspiciously, as he feels Johnny's sack*): Maybe you carry a pistol in your sack. (*Frowning, as he feels it.*) What strange weapon do you have in here?

JOHNNY APPLESEED (*setting sack on ground, reaching inside*): I'll show you. (*With clearly defined movements he takes a seed, holds it up to Indians, digs a small hole, plants seed, steps back, gestures toward covered hole.*) In a few years a beautiful tree will blossom from this very spot. It will bear delicious apples—enough for both your people and mine.

THIRD INDIAN (*with a puzzled expression as he takes a handful of seeds from sack*): Apples? From these seeds?

THIRD CHILD (*to Johnny, as tension relaxes somewhat*): You

must be Johnny Appleseed! We've heard all about you! (*The children and mothers smile and mutter in agreement.*)

FIRST INDIAN (*frowning in confusion*): Johnny Appleseed? (*To other Indians.*) We have not heard of such a man.

SECOND INDIAN (*sourly, suspiciously*): It's another trick to take more of our lands. (*Other Indians growl their agreement.*)

THIRD INDIAN (*scowling with finality as he takes the arm of one of the mothers*): You will come as our prisoners. Your warriors will be sorry for their wickedness.

JOHNNY APPLESEED (*to Indians, sternly, boldly*): You will return to your village alone. (*Surprised by such boldness, the Third Indian releases mother's arm. Johnny now appeals to the Indians' curiosity.*) Let me show you something. (*Taking a large, shiny apple from the sack, he holds it up.*) Here is a token of our friendship. (*Handing apple to an Indian.*) Here—taste it. (*One at a time, the curious Indians bite the apple, nod with pleasure.*)

FIRST INDIAN (*admiring the apple*): This is magic fruit! Where did you find it?

SECOND INDIAN (*reaching for sack which Johnny opens for him*): We'd like more. (*Second Indian takes another apple from sack.*)

JOHNNY APPLESEED: You can have all the apples you wish. But you must promise to live peacefully with your neighbors.

THIRD INDIAN (*doubtfully, suspiciously*): You are tricking us again. You hope to trade us a few apples for our forests and lakes. (*To other Indians.*) Let's take our prisoners!

JOHNNY APPLESEED (*calmly but sternly blocking the way to the right wing*): Stop! I may be old, but you'll think you've tangled with a grizzly bear. (*As the Indians hesitate, the Fourth Indian enters from right, hailing Johnny.*)

FOURTH INDIAN (*in friendly greeting*): Johnny Appleseed! Welcome, old friend! (*Fourth Indian and Johnny exchange greetings by placing hands on each other's shoulder.*)

JOHNNY APPLESEED: How are you, Running Elk? It's been many moons since we planted your apple orchards.

FOURTH INDIAN (*commanding other Indians*): Get back! (*As the Indians retreat, the Fourth Indian explains to them.*) It's true that there are wicked settlers, just as there are evil warriors in our own tribes. But this man is our friend. He has shown my tribe how to grow great orchards that give us food and shelter. (*The other Indians turn curiously toward Johnny.*)

FIRST INDIAN (*to Johnny*): Will you teach us how to make the earth bloom with your magic trees?

FOURTH INDIAN (*to Indians*): Johnny has restless feet; he does not stay long in one valley. But my people will teach you of Johnny's magic. (*The three Indians briefly huddle to talk things over.*)

SECOND INDIAN (*holding up palm*): We are friends from this day on. Together we will share the land.

JOHNNY APPLESEED (*to Fourth Indian*): Thank you for bringing peace between our peoples. (*Throwing sack over shoulder.*) Good-by for now. (*The Indians wave and happily exit at right. The settlers crowd around Johnny, murmuring:* Thank you . . . Please return . . . Johnny Appleseed!)

SECOND CHILD: Think of all the wonderful things that his trees give us—like apple pies and apple juice!

THIRD CHILD: And cool shade on hot days!

FIRST CHILD: And what's more fun than swinging from an apple tree!

JOHNNY APPLESEED (*smiling, giving a handful of seeds to a child*): Perhaps you will help me by planting these. A hundred years from now folks may have apples descended from these very seeds. (*Waving good-by, he wanders toward left while looking around for planting areas.*)

FIRST MOTHER (*as all wave good-by to Johnny*): Good-by . . . we'll always remember your wonderful work.

SECOND CHILD: Good-by, Johnny Appleseed! (*Curtain falls.*)

Sir Galahad and the Maidens

CHARACTERS

Narrator	First Brother
Sir Galahad	Second Brother
Old Man	Third Brother
Young Man	Fourth Brother
First Maiden	Fifth Brother
Second Maiden	Sixth Brother
Third Maiden	Seventh Brother
Fourth Maiden	Castle Extras

INTRODUCTION BY NARRATOR

Ladies and gentlemen, we are about to journey back to the exciting times of King Arthur and his knights of the Round Table. Perhaps you remember some of the characters who appeared in these famous tales: Merlin the Magician, Queen Guinevere, and those dashing knights named Sir Lancelot and Sir Tristram.

Tonight's scene tells the story of one of the most gallant of all the knights privileged to sit with King Arthur at his Round Table. We shall witness one of the thrilling adventures of Sir Galahad, that brave, heroic, and courteous knight in armor. Our scene is entitled "Sir Galahad and the Maidens."

Late one morning, after winning several battles for his king and after rescuing some fair maidens in distress, Sir Galahad found himself riding along a strange and silent valley. Before him there suddenly appeared a mysterious-looking castle. He was surprised to find himself at its gates, for he had expected to discover nothing more in this quiet valley than a few wild birds or perhaps a woodcutter or two. Our story begins as Sir Galahad dismounts from his horse and stands in astonishment at the entrance to the mysterious castle. (*Narrator exits. Curtain rises.*)

SETTING AT RISE OF CURTAIN

The setting is a courtyard just outside the castle's main gate. Plants, crockery, and a bench or two may be set in the background. Other items common to the Middle Ages, such as lances, shields, and buckets, may also be displayed. Sir Galahad stands near the left wing, with shield and drawn sword. (All swords are made of cardboard.)

SIR GALAHAD (*calling toward opposite wing*): Ho, there! A stranger bids to enter your castle! I am Sir Galahad, knight of the Round Table. I bring you greetings in the name of noble King Arthur! (*After a brief pause, the Old Man totters out from right, followed by the Young Man.*)

OLD MAN (*peering closely at Sir Galahad, shaking his head*): Son, I beseech you to seek lodgings elsewhere. The brave champion of King Arthur will find only sorrow here.

SIR GALAHAD: Pray tell me, sir, what is the name of this silent castle?

YOUNG MAN: It is silent because it is sorrowful. It is called the Castle of Maidens. All the fair ladies who dwell here are captives within its walls. . . .

(*The four Maidens stealthily enter from right, glancing anxiously over their shoulders. They are followed by Extras. The Young Man gestures toward the Maidens.*)

OLD MAN: From their own lips you will hear of their distress.

FIRST MAIDEN (*as Maidens approach Sir Galahad*): Brave knight, sir, please turn aside from this wicked place.

SECOND MAIDEN: At once! We implore you! You are in mortal danger.

SIR GALAHAD: What is the mystery here? Why do you warn me against the Castle of Maidens?

THIRD MAIDEN (*glancing fearfully about, she inquires of the others*): Is it safe to speak? (*Asking in stage whisper.*) Where are the seven wicked brothers?

FOURTH MAIDEN (*gesturing furtively*): I think . . . I think they are on the far side repairing their armor. We cannot linger here for long.

OLD MAN (*to Sir Galahad*): All of us who live within the Castle of Maidens are prisoners of the seven wicked brothers. We cannot leave as we wish . . . nor can strangers enter its walls without peril to their lives.

SIR GALAHAD: So this is a captive castle.

OLD MAN (*sadly*): Yes . . . our chains grow heavier every day.

SIR GALAHAD: I wish to hear more.

YOUNG MAN: It all started many years ago when the seven brothers came here as guests of Duke Lianor. They betrayed the good duke and took possession of the castle and its inhabitants. (*Sternly.*) They are hard and angry men without a trace of mercy. (*Reminiscently.*) But one day something happened which frightened them. The duke's daughter prophecied that on some bright day a gallant knight would overcome their wickedness and restore freedom to the people.

OLD MAN: That is why you must leave at once. The wicked brothers are desperately afraid of visitors. If they should find you here. . . .

FIRST MAIDEN (*quickly glancing toward right wing, holding up a hand for silence*): Listen! I hear the sound of their armor. (*In alarm.*) They are coming! (*Pleading.*) Please, sir knight, turn and flee. To remain here means your very life. (*As the seven Brothers angrily enter from right, the Maidens and the Extras cry out and race offstage at left. Sir Galahad stoutly faces the Brothers.*)

FIRST BROTHER (*standing with spread legs before Sir Galahad, contemptuously eyeing him up and down*): You will wish, sir intruder, that you had heeded the warning of our fair ladies. Now you may find it too late.

SECOND BROTHER (*smirking, as all Brothers approach Sir Galahad in a threatening manner*): Unless, of course, you choose to show us the speed of a frightened deer. Be off with you!

OLD MAN: Please obey his command, Sir Galahad.

YOUNG MAN: We would not think you cowardly, sir. Your single sword cannot fairly match their seven.

THIRD BROTHER (*laughing*): Ah, the young squire speaks the truth. One puny sword against seven of the mightiest blades in all the land. Ho! (*The Brothers swiftly draw their swords, holding them ready for action.*)

SIR GALAHAD (*calmly, bravely*): One sword against seven? I tell you, sirs, it would be an unfair match indeed. I am used to doing battle with at least ten swords. (*Holding his sword in position for attack.*) However, if you insist upon battle, I must take unfair advantage of you. (*Crouching.*) Are you ready, sirs? (*The Brothers are somewhat shaken at Sir Galahad's calm confidence.*)

FOURTH BROTHER (*to his brothers, sourly and with amazement*): A bold fellow we have here . . . the likes of which we have not seen before. Shall we finish with his insolent words?

FIFTH BROTHER (*shaking his sword*): Let's be done with him! (*Jeering.*) King Arthur will soon find a vacant chair at his Round Table.

SIXTH BROTHER (*shaking his head, holding up a restraining arm before his brothers*): Wait, brethren. I am enjoying this comical fellow. It is a long time since we have had so much amusement. A court jester—that's what he is—the king's clown! (*The Brothers laugh, relax somewhat.*)

SEVENTH BROTHER (*looking at the sky, pointing toward the sun with his sword*): Sir Clown, you may continue to amuse us until the sun reaches the top of the sky. (*Growling.*) But take heed, if we find you still here at noon of day you will have a chance to prove your sword. You will think yourself struck by seven bolts of lightning. (*Laughing, waving sword.*) By all means entertain our fair maidens. (*Jeering.*) But take care that we do not entertain ourselves with you. (*The Brothers replace their swords and start to exit at right while chuckling and ad libbing remarks, such as:* Ha! . . . One sword against seven . . . Foolish knight. *As they exit, all the previous characters enter cautiously from left. Sir Galahad replaces his sword in scabbard.*)

SECOND MAIDEN (*with admiration*): Sir Galahad! You are the first noble knight to tame those wicked men!

THIRD MAIDEN: Welcome, brave sir! (*Tilting head in sudden wonder, speaking to others.*) Is it possible that he is the answer to the prophecy? Can we hope to be saved at last?

OLD MAN (*nodding soberly*): It is the right time of the year for the prophecy to be fulfilled. It may well be that Sir Galahad is our champion and deliverer.

SIR GALAHAD: I know not whether I have been sent here as an instrument of justice, but I assure you that I will not depart until freedom and honor have been restored. (*The others murmur their admiration.*)

YOUNG MAN (*glancing nervously at sky*): The hour of noon approaches. . . .

SIR GALAHAD: Then I beg all of you to return to your rooms within the castle. I will not have you endanger your lives.

OLD MAN (*indicating himself and the Young Man*): We shall remain . . . perhaps we can help in some small way. It is our battle, too.

SIR GALAHAD (*gallantly*): Thank you, sirs, but no. Please escort the ladies to safety.

FOURTH MAIDEN (*nodding emphatically, speaking with certainty*): Truly he is the one sent to deliver us. Heaven's greatest blessing upon you, brave knight. (*The others agree by ad libbing:* Brave Sir Galahad . . . Stout heart . . . Our champion.)

SIR GALAHAD (*swiftly drawing his sword, waving it*): Into the castle! Hasten! (*As they reluctantly start to exit at right, the Old Man lingers, holding up arms toward Sir Galahad in blessing.*)

OLD MAN: Righteousness shall be your sword and shield! (*Others exit as Sir Galahad glances at sun, walks cautiously about. He turns toward right wing, as if expecting the Brothers to appear there.*)

FIRST BROTHER (*unexpectedly leaping onstage from left, waving sword*): Welcome to my blade, foolish knight! (*They duel, while working their way toward right wing. First Brother staggers offstage, holding his wounded side. The moment he exits the Second Brother leaps in from right.*)

SECOND BROTHER (*shouting*): Perish! (*They duel furiously; the Second Brother, wounded, crawls offstage at right while groaning. The Third Brother charges in immediately from opposite wing. After a brief duel he also falls offstage at right. Sir Galahad leaps to stage center as the Fourth and Fifth Brothers appear at left wing and the Sixth and Seventh Brothers appear at right wing.*)

FOURTH BROTHER (*as Brothers slowly close in on Sir Galahad*): Our brothers shall be avenged!

SIXTH BROTHER (*as Brothers charge Sir Galahad*): At him! Give him our steel! (*A furious duel takes place. Sir Galahad is driven backward at first, but manages to nick the Fourth Brother who howls and reels offstage. At this point Sir Galahad takes the offensive; as he thrusts with quickened energy the remaining three brothers are driven backward toward the left wing. The Fifth Brother tosses aside his sword and flees offstage at left; the remaining pair fight desperately for a moment longer, then also turn and race off at left. Lest they return, Sir Galahad remains on guard for a moment. He then replaces his sword, turns away from left wing. All the previous characters joyously troop in from right. They surround Sir Galahad.)*

FIRST MAIDEN: Well done, sir!

SECOND MAIDEN (*gesturing toward right wing*): I was watching from the tower window. The seven wicked brothers are riding away as if pursued by an army!

THIRD MAIDEN: We are free at last. We are forever grateful to you!

OLD MAN (*gesturing toward right wing*): Come and lodge with us in our captive . . . I mean in our free castle. We welcome you as our honored guest.

FOURTH MAIDEN: Yes, please tarry with us for awhile.

SIR GALAHAD: Thank you, kind people, but there are many more adventures yet to come. I must ride on once more. Who knows what other castles may be in need of King Arthur's knights? (*Raising arm.*) I bid you all a fond farewell. (*The others wave good-by while ad libbing:* Peace be with you . . . Farewell, noble champion . . . We shall always remember your brave deed. *Sir Galahad exits at left as the others continue to wave. Curtain descends.*)

HAPPY HOLIDAYS FOR LITTLE WOMEN

CHARACTERS

Narrator	Mother March
Jo March	Laurie
Amy March	First Young Man
Beth March	Second Young Man
Meg March	Third Young Man

INTRODUCTION BY NARRATOR

Welcome, ladies and gentlemen. One of the most beloved classics of American literature is a story written by Louisa May Alcott. It is entitled *Little Women*. I'm sure that many of you have read this book about the four March sisters—Jo, Amy, Beth and Meg. Tonight, our actors and actresses will present a scene which is based on several incidents in the lives of our little women. The time is evening, shortly before Christmas of 1864. The place is the parlor of our four young heroines.

SETTING AT RISE OF CURTAIN

The parlor is set with the usual furnishings of a home during the Civil War period. A table is set at center stage. A few simple, homemade Christmas ornaments, such as a holly wreath and a picture of Santa Claus, are displayed in background.

Jo is lying on the rug with a book propped up in front of her.

AMY (*entering from right with a dress and sewing equipment*): Jo, what do you think of this old dress? How can I fix it up for Christmas? (*Jo ignores her, continuing to read.*) Jo March! I spoke to you! (*As Jo still ignores her, Amy sighs indignantly, sits and works on the dress. Beth and Meg enter from right carrying dresses and sewing baskets. Amy holds her dress up to them.*) Meg, you're the one with all the imagination around here. Do some imagining for me on this.

MEG (*setting down her basket, examining Amy's dress, sadly shaking head*): I can't imagine this for Christmas. It's hopeless. (*Fingering her own dress.*) And just look at mine. It's so dreadful to be poor.

JO (*looking up from book*): Christmas won't be Christmas without something new and pretty.

BETH (*sewing*): Mother thinks it best that we go without presents this year. After all, it won't be much of a holiday season for father. (*Hopefully.*) Maybe the army will let him come home for a visit. Wouldn't that be wonderful!

AMY (*sadly*): When will this frightful war end? I guess President Lincoln is doing his best to bring peace.

JO (*cheerfully*): Someday I'll write an exciting book that everyone will want to read. Then we'll have plenty of Christmas presents!

MEG (*to Jo*): Why don't you stop dreaming and get out and really earn some money? Take me—teaching stubborn little children their lessons. (*Sighing.*) I pay a high price for being the eldest of the four March sisters.

BETH (*reproving Meg*): You can just stop feeling sorry for yourself, Miss Meg March. And the rest of us, too. Christmas is supposed to be a merry season, no matter how poor you are. (*Examining her sewing.*) At least we can make it a merry Christmas for mother, even if it's only a pair of gloves. (*There is silence for a moment as Jo reads and the others sew.*)

JO (*while looking at book*): When will mother be home?

AMY: Soon, I think. (*Holding up an oddly shaped piece of cloth.*) Now what in the world can I do with this rag?

MEG (*giggling*): Make a witch's mask. At least it's something you can wear.

AMY (*indignantly, as the others giggle*): You're so funny. Just you wait. I'll turn it into some lovely handkerchiefs. You'll see how clever I am. (*They again fall into silence.*)

JO (*snapping book shut, rising, stretching*): We need something active to do. (*Brightly.*) I know! We'll rehearse the Christmas play. Let's see who's the best actress.

BETH: How?

JO: We'll take turns acting out the same scene. Like this! (*Clasping hands, staggering across the room, pleading dramatically.*) Roderigo! Save me! Please, Roderigo! Save me! (*To Beth, in normal voice.*) Your turn.

BETH (*shyly, reluctantly*): Must I? (*The others firmly nod. Beth acts out the scene shyly and self-consciously, without much dramatic expression.*) Roderigo. Save me. Roderigo. Save me. (*Shrugging apologetically.*) That's the best I can do.

MEG (*stepping confidently forward*): I'll show you how a real actress does it. (*With exaggerated dramatics she acts out the scene.*) Roderigo! Roderigo! Save me! Please, sir! Save me! (*Demanding of others.*) Applause, please.

AMY (*clapping once only, stepping to stage center*): I'll try it. (*She performs stiffly, primly.*) Roderigo. Please save me. Roderigo, do you hear me? Roderigo. (*To others, in self-defense.*) Anyway, I don't claim to be an actress. (*Returning to her basket.*) Let's get on with our sewing. (*There is a short silence once more as Jo reads while the others sew.*)

JO (*looking up*): We do want to make it a merry Christmas for mother. Here we sit around and complain while mother has more problems than the rest of us put together. (*Tilting ear*

toward wing, leaping up.) Here she comes! Hide your sewing! (*The girls quickly set their baskets in back of chairs.*)

MOTHER (*cheerfully entering from left*): Glad to find you so merry, my girls!

BETH (*running to Mother who puts an arm around her*): Mother!

MOTHER (*inspecting the girls*): Jo, you look tired. Mustn't study too hard. How is your cold, Meg? (*As Amy rushes offstage at right, the others help Mother with her coat, lead her to a chair at center table.*)

AMY (*returning with tea on tray*): We kept the tea hot for you, Mother. (*All sit around table as Amy pours tea.*)

MOTHER (*smiling*): After supper I'll have a surprise for you.

MEG (*excitedly*): A surprise! (*Pleading.*) May we have it now? Please?

JO (*soberly sighing*): We want a surprise so badly.

BETH (*eagerly asking*): Is it something about Christmas? (*Explosively.*) I know what it is! Father's coming home! (*Almost weeping.*) Will father be here for Christmas?

MOTHER (*taking a letter from her handbag on table*): No, children, I'm afraid the army still needs him. (*Cheerfully waving envelope.*) But he did write us a nice long letter. We'll have to be satisfied with that for now. (*She slowly takes letter from envelope.*)

AMY (*impatiently*): Hurry, mother!

MOTHER (*unfolding letter*): You can read the details later on, but your father tells of his days around the campfires and on the battlefield. A soldier's day is hard and dreary, but he's not one to complain.

MEG: That's just like him. No matter how dreadful, he tries to make things sound easy. That's so we won't worry too much. Dear, dear father.

JO (*indignantly*): Why did they have to take him, anyway? He's so much older than the others.

MOTHER (*explaining*): The army needs chaplains just as much as it needs captains and generals. Your father reads the Bible to wounded men; tries to give them hope and courage. They need him almost as much as we do. (*Indicating letter.*) I'll read you the part of his message especially for you. (*Reading.*) Give them all my dear love and a kiss. Tell them I think of them by day, pray for them by night, and find my best comfort in their affection at all times. I know that when I come back to them I may be fonder and prouder than ever of my little women. (*All girls sniffle, as two of them touch handkerchiefs to eyes.*)

AMY (*sobbing, hiding her head on Mother's shoulder*): I'm so ashamed of my selfishness. (*Reproving herself.*) Fussing over a Christmas dress when father is out there!

BETH (*with determination*): We'll try very hard to make him proud of us.

MOTHER (*tenderly patting nearest girl*): Of course you will. (*Changing the mood to cheeriness.*) Now, then, suppose we have our tea while we make some plans. After all, we have both Christmas and New Year's Day to celebrate! (*Smiling, peering at baskets behind chairs.*) Do I see sewing baskets? Suppose you bring them out where I can help. (*As the girls take baskets there is a knock on the door.*) Jo, get the door. (*Jo lightly races off at left.*)

MEG (*brightly*): Maybe it's Santa Claus!

AMY (*to Meg, grinning*): Silly goose! (*Jo enters from left with Laurie, a pleasant and somewhat shy young man in his teens.*)

LAURIE: Good evening, Mrs. March . . . Meg, Beth, Amy.

MOTHER: How are you, Laurie? Join us in tea?

LAURIE (*sitting, somewhat bashfully*): I can stay only a few minutes. I . . . I just wanted to ask about New Year's Eve. Are . . . are you girls doing anything?

MEG (*grinning, posing with dramatic gestures*): I don't know about my poor sisters, but I am attending the royal ball!

BETH: Meg, stop it! (*To Laurie, eagerly.*) We're not doing anything that we can't set aside!

AMY (*expectantly*): If it's a party invitation our answer is yes.

MOTHER (*smiling, reproving*): Girls!

LAURIE (*nodding*): I've been asked to help with a New Year's party.

Jo (*eagerly*): Who will be there?

LAURIE (*gesturing toward left wing*): Three of the fellows are waiting outside right now.

MOTHER (*surprised*): Out in the chilly night? (*To Jo.*) Jo, you get them in here at once. (*Smiling at Laurie as Jo exits at left.*) You needn't fear that my daughters will bite them.

LAURIE: It isn't that, Mrs. March. They're afraid they're not dressed properly. They just came from their work at the factory.

BETH (*to her sisters in dismay*): Dressed! (*Gasping, glancing at her dress.*) How awful we look!

LAURIE (*studying Beth*): You look good to me.

AMY (*as the three sisters leap up and start toward right*): We just can't entertain guests looking like this! (*The girls squeal while racing offstage at right. Mother smiles at the surprised Laurie.*)

MOTHER: That's the way little women behave sometimes. You'll just have to get used to them. (*Jo enters with the three young men. Greetings are ad libbed between Mother and the young men.*)

FIRST YOUNG MAN (*to Jo, glancing around in disappointment*): Where are your sisters? I was hoping they'd be here.

MOTHER (*rising*): They'll be back in a moment. Please take off your coats while I prepare tea and cakes. You must be frozen. (*The young men remove their coats as Mother exits at right with the tea tray. The boys stand or sit.*)

Jo (*eagerly*): I understand you fellows will be at the New Year's party. (*Hinting.*) Are you taking anyone special? (*The offstage girls giggle as if excitedly primping. The boys exchange surprised glances and stare toward right wing. Jo tries to distract them.*) Uh . . . cold weather we're having for winter. (*The giggles grow louder.*)

SECOND YOUNG MAN (*somewhat absently, as the boys blink toward right wing.*) Uh . . . yes . . . funny that it's colder in winter than in summer.

THIRD YOUNG MAN (*staring, absently nodding*): Yes . . . lovely weather we're having this summer. (*As the giggles abruptly cease, the three girls enter. They are more colorfully dressed, with additions of hair ribbons and jewelry.*)

MEG (*assuming surprise at seeing the boys*): Well! Hello! (*Apologizing.*) Sorry we missed you when you first came; we were in the other room.

JO (*somewhat sarcastically*): Yes, we heard you. (*All exchange ad lib greetings.*)

FIRST YOUNG MAN: Mrs. Gardiner is giving a New Year's party. If you'd like to come, there'll be all kinds of fun. Do you like to dance? (*The girls eagerly ad lib together:* Yes! . . . Very much! . . . I do!)

SECOND YOUNG MAN (*grinning, stepping to center stage*): How about practicing right now? That is, if it's all right with your mother.

MOTHER (*entering, nodding, placing tray on table*): You young folks go right ahead and have a good time. Be sure to try my fruit cookies. (*Mother exits at right.*)

THIRD YOUNG MAN (*bowing playfully to any one of the girls*): May I have this dance? (*For the next few minutes they pair off to dance, chat, laugh, munch cookies, and have a good time in general. If desired, one of the couples may perform an exhibition dance which the others applaud. Offstage music may accompany their dancing. Finally, Laurie takes his coat.*)

LAURIE (*calling*): Come on, fellows; time to go.

MEG (*disappointed*): Oh, no! Can't you stay a little longer?

FIRST YOUNG MAN: Wish we could, Miss Meg, but we've got to get up early tomorrow morning. The war makes lots of extra work for everyone.

SECOND YOUNG MAN (*to girls*): Just you wait till New Year's Eve. We'll make up for lost time. (*The girls help the boys with their coats as all ad lib pleasant remarks, such as:* Don't catch cold . . . Thank you for the invitation . . . Come again, soon.)

THIRD YOUNG MAN (*as boys are ready to exit at left wing*): Good-by. Please thank your mother for us.

LAURIE (*holding up finger*): Don't forget—New Year's Eve! (*As the boys exit at left, the girls follow them offstage as both groups again ad lib their farewells. Mother enters at right, looks toward left wing, smiling as she hears the offstage chatter. As she places the teacups back on the tray, the girls joyously race back, laughing and shouting ad libs, such as:* Happy holidays! . . . Three cheers for Christmas! . . . Won't it be fun? . . . Hooray! *They suddenly notice Mother.*)

AMY (*bursting with joy, hugging Mother*): Guess what, mother?

BETH (*also bursting*): We're invited to a New Year's party! I'm sure Mrs. Gardiner will want you, too.

MOTHER (*gently smiling*): Your shining faces are enough for me. I'm sure it will be happy holidays for my little women.

MEG (*gasping*): Our party dresses! We've got to get busy!

JO: Let's see what we can find in the closet. (*To Mother.*) Will you help us, mother?

MOTHER: Of course, dears. A little needle and thread will turn you into four lovely princesses. (*The girls gaily race off at right as Mother sighs and picks up the tea tray.*)

BETH (*poking head onstage*): Hurry, mother! (*Beth disappears.*)

MOTHER (*calling toward right*): Coming, girls! (*She replaces the tea tray on the table, picks up a sewing basket, smiles, nods, sighs deeply as she walks toward right.*) Yes, I'm sure it will be happy holidays for the four little women . . . my precious little women. (*Mother exits. Curtain descends.*)

David and Goliath

CHARACTERS

Narrator

David

Goliath

First Soldier

Second Soldier

Third Soldier

First Woman

Second Woman

Third Woman

Fourth Woman

Fifth Woman

King Saul

Extra Soldiers

INTRODUCTION BY NARRATOR

Good evening, ladies and gentlemen, and welcome to tonight's play. You are about to see a short drama entitled "David and Goliath" which is based on the classic story from the Old Testament.

Perhaps you recall that the armies of Israel and the forces of the Philistines were camped on opposite mountains, ready for battle. Perhaps you also remember that when they finally clashed in the valley between them, the Israelites drove the Philistines back in defeat. Tonight's play will show you how and why the armies of Israel were able to conquer their enemies. The time of our play is shortly before the beginning of the battle. (*Narrator exits. Curtain rises.*)

SETTING AT RISE OF CURTAIN

The background is set with shrubbery, grass and rocks. The rest of the stage is bare, except for small clusters of bushes.

The three Israelite soldiers creep cautiously onstage from right, armed with shields and cardboard swords. They motion to each other as they silently work toward the left. When reaching left stage they crouch behind shrubbery and peer anxiously into left wing.

FIRST SOLDIER (*in dismay*): The Philistine army appears as ten thousand ants. How shall we stand before them?

SECOND SOLDIER (*continuing to peer*): Fear not; the Lord is mightier than all their arms. He shall give us the victory. (*The five women, plus Extras if desired, cautiously enter from right.*)

FIRST WOMAN (*calling softly to soldiers*): How goes it? Does the enemy advance?

THIRD SOLDIER (*angrily gesturing toward the women*): Back—stay back! (*The women retreat a step or two, huddling fearfully.*)

FIRST SOLDIER (*rising, gesturing toward left wing in astonishment*): Look! A single Philistine approaches!

SECOND SOLDIER (*amazed, as soldiers stare*): A giant of a man —as tall as a sycamore! Back! (*The soldiers retreat to stage center where they crouch toward left wing in battle postures.*)

DAVID (*entering from right, carrying a sack of food*): Brethren, I bring bread and cheese to strengthen your arms . . . .

THIRD SOLDIER (*whirling to David, interrupting*): Drop your sack and be off! This is no place for a shepherd boy. (*To soldiers, as he gestures toward left.*) He comes!

(*David sets sack down, remains near right wing, apart from the women. Goliath struts heavily onstage from left, plants his feet wide apart, arrogantly looks around. He is tall, darkly bearded, clad in armor, and carrying a blunt spear made of wood or cardboard tubing. The women gasp.*)

GOLIATH (*booming defiantly*): Hear me, men of Israel! I am Goliath, champion from the camp of the Philistines! I challenge you to send me your mightiest warrior for combat. If I slay your champion your people shall become our slaves. But if I fall before your warrior, my people shall be your servants. Ho! (*He makes an X mark on the ground with his spear.*) Choose your champion and send him here within the hour! (*Goliath looks contemptuously around, laughs viciously, thumps his spear against the ground, struts offstage at left.*)

SECOND WOMAN (*in distress*): What shall we do? We have no giant equal to the fierce Philistine.

DAVID (*confidently*): Brethren, have no fear of the heathen giant. Whoever fights him shall have the strength of the Lord's right arm.

THIRD WOMAN (*to David, somewhat scornfully*): Why do you linger, shepherd boy? Return to the safety of your flock.

DAVID (*boldly stepping forward*): This is the hour of our deliverance. I, David, son of Jesse, will go and fight him. (*The others mutter and jeer somewhat.*)

FOURTH WOMAN (*looking into right wing, gesturing*): King Saul approaches!

(*King Saul, dressed in bright, royal garments, enters with great dignity from right. If desired, he may be followed by Extra Soldiers. The Israelites bow, open the way for him to pass through.*)

FIRST SOLDIER (*saluting King Saul*): King Saul, the mighty Goliath has challenged us to send a champion against him. Where will we find a man strong enough to slay him?

KING SAUL (*looking around*): Is there not a single man of courage among you? (*The soldiers hang their heads.*) Is there not one of you with the heart of a giant?

DAVID (*bowing to King Saul*): Let your servant David go forth for you. I have no fear of the Philistine. (*The crowd mutters its disapproval.*)

FIFTH WOMAN (*shaking head at David*): Can a sparrow slay a hawk?

KING SAUL (*with kindness, nodding to David*): You are but a frail youth, while the giant is the mightiest warrior in his camp.

DAVID (*eagerly holding up hands*): When a lion and a bear attacked my father's flock I slew them with my bare hands. So shall I do to the Philistine. The Lord who delivered me from the lion and the bear shall deliver me from this wicked one. (*King Saul ponders for a moment while studying David.*)

KING SAUL (*suddenly exclaiming*): So be it! (*To Second Soldier.*) Give him your sword and shield!

SECOND SOLDIER (*protesting, shaking head*): King Saul, I fear we are lost. Let us at least send forth our mightiest captain.

KING SAUL (*decisively*): The choice is final. David shall be our champion. (*To David.*) Go with our prayers. (*Second Soldier offers his sword to David.*)

DAVID (*refusing sword*): I wish neither sword nor shield. (*He opens a small bag tied to his waist and takes out a sling.*) My weapons shall be this sling and five smooth stones. (*He quickly searches about and picks up five imaginary stones which he places in the bag. Goliath roars* Ho! *from offstage.*)

FIRST WOMAN (*alarmed, motioning toward left*): Goliath comes! (*The Israelites gasp and fearfully cluster behind King Saul at right stage. King Saul himself stands tall and unafraid. David takes imaginary stone from bag, sets it in sling, ready for action at center stage.*)

GOLIATH (*strutting arrogantly onstage from left, glancing disdainfully around, shouting*): Where is your mighty champion? I see but a lowly shepherd boy before me. (*To David, laughing.*) Am I a dog that you meet me with sling and stone? Ha!

DAVID (*boldly taking a quick step forward*): You come to me with a stout spear, but I stand before you in the name of the God of Israel. This very hour shall you fall before me!

GOLIATH (*approaching, raising spear, jeering*): The champion shepherd boy! Ha! (*For a few seconds they shift positions around stage, preparing to attack. Goliath strikes out several times toward David who nimbly leaps aside. As Goliath snarls and again prepares to lunge, David adjusts the imaginary stone in the sling, whirls it around and overhead and lets it fly. Goliath cries out, clapping a hand to his forehead as he staggers toward downstage left. He collapses, falling outstretched on his back. David races over, raises his arms overhead in a gesture of victory as he stands astride Goliath.*)

DAVID (*victoriously*): The Lord has given victory to His people!

SECOND WOMAN (*triumphantly*): The shepherd boy has conquered our enemy! Hail, David! (*All cheer.*)

THIRD WOMAN (*peering into left wing, motioning, shouting*): Look! The Philistines scatter like straws in the wind!

FOURTH WOMAN (*as all joyously look into left wing*): Without their champion they are lost!

FIFTH WOMAN: The battle is ours! (*All cheer.*)

KING SAUL (*commanding soldiers, gesturing broadly*): Blow the trumpets! Sound the advance! Our armies shall finish the enemy! (*As an offstage trumpet blows, the soldiers wave their swords, shout triumphantly and charge offstage at left. King Saul calls to David.*) Riches and honor shall be your reward. (*Motioning toward left wing.*) Go! Give us the full victory! (*David raises a palm in recognition of King Saul's command, turns and races offstage at left. The women cheer as the curtain falls.*)

The Return
of Rip Van Winkle

CHARACTERS

Narrator	Fourth Citizen
Man who Whittles	Fifth Citizen
Man with Newspaper	Sixth Citizen
Rip Van Winkle	Seventh Citizen
First Child	Eighth Citizen
Second Child	Ninth Citizen
Third Child	Tenth Citizen
The Mayor	Old Woman
First Citizen	Old Man
Second Citizen	Extra Citizens
Third Citizen	

INTRODUCTION BY NARRATOR

Good evening, ladies and gentlemen. You are about to witness a scene from one of the great classics of American literature. This will be a dramatic presentation based upon the story of *Rip Van Winkle*, written by Washington Irving. Our scene is entitled "The Return of Rip Van Winkle."

Washington Irving opens his tale with a description of the countryside in which the events take place. Rip Van Winkle and his family lived in a small village at the foot of the Catskill

Mountains in New York State. This region was originally settled by Dutch colonists who tilled the soil, gathered their crops, and taught their children to read, write and live as liberty-loving Americans.

The early part of Washington Irving's story also tells us something about the character of Rip Van Winkle himself. This likeable fellow enjoyed nothing better than roaming the hills and valleys in search of adventure. He always carried his old-fashioned rifle, and his faithful dog Wolf accompanied him wherever he went. It was during one of these hunting expeditions that a very strange thing happened to Rip Van Winkle. It seems that he fell asleep. Now this isn't so strange in itself, but no one —before or after—ever had such a peculiar sleep as Rip Van Winkle. For one thing, he slept for twenty years! And when he finally woke up . . . well, this is where our exciting story begins. (*Narrator exits. Curtain rises.*)

SETTING AT RISE OF CURTAIN

The scene opens on the main street of a small mountain village, shortly after the American Revolution. A vacant bench is at upstage center. On another bench at upstage right sit the Man who Whittles and the Man with Newspaper.

MAN WHO WHITTLES (*lazily stretching*): Lazy day . . . lazy day. . . . (*To Man with Newspaper*). What's the news today? What has General Washington been doing? I suppose our Congress is busy making new laws for the new nation. (*Nodding in appreciation.*) Bless those brave lads who went through Valley Forge. Bless our free and independent country.

MAN WITH NEWSPAPER (*after reading a moment longer*): I see that we'll be holding some more elections. Now that the war of guns is over we'll be having a war of words. (*Closes paper, stretching.*) Already our war for independence seems far away and long ago. As you say, squire, it's just another lazy day

(*Looks around.*) Nothing much seems to happen in our peaceful little village.

MAN WHO WHITTLES: Yesterday the baker's horse ran wild and trampled the mayor's garden . . . if you can call that exciting. (*Looks up, sees Rip Van Winkle, who is still offstage left, approaching.*) Well, who is this stumbling old fellow coming into town?

MAN WITH NEWSPAPER (*also peering offstage left*): A peddler, most likely. He doesn't seem to have anything to sell. (*They fall into silence, continue to whittle and read.*)

(*Rip Van Winkle, bearded and carrying a rusty rifle, slowly enters from left wing. He gazes around in bewilderment, falters, moves forward a few steps, rubs his eyes. A man and woman enter from right wing, cross toward him.*)

RIP VAN WINKLE (*speaking hopefully to couple*): Good day, neighbors. (*They stare blankly at him, pause briefly, pass by. He speaks as they pass.*) Please, can you tell me . . . (*He breaks off as they ignore him and exit at left. He wanders about, inspecting the street. He looks around, trying to find familiar sights, mutters as he fails to do so.*) Everything seems so strange, so different . . . so many new houses. (*Looking upward.*) Where are all the familiar old rooftops I used to look upon from my mountain-top?

(*First, Second and Third Child gaily enter from right, catch sight of Rip Van Winkle, curiously approach him.*)

FIRST CHILD (*greeting Rip pleasantly*): Hello. Are you a stranger to our village?

SECOND CHILD: Maybe you are the grandfather of one of our schoolmates.

THIRD CHILD: My grandfather's beard is not nearly as long as yours.

FIRST CHILD: When I am a grandfather I will want to have a beard just as long and fine as yours.

SECOND CHILD: Sir, you look very tired and hungry. (*Reaches into pocket, pulls out piece of bread.*) Here, take a piece of bread. It will make you strong and healthy. (*Second Child stuffs piece of bread into Rip Van Winkle's pocket as the old man nods his thanks. The three children playfully exit at left.*)

RIP VAN WINKLE (*again looking around, speaking sadly*): Even the faces are strange . . . (*Suddenly remembering, speaking with spirit.*) And where is my dog, Wolf? (*Turns around, calling.*) Here, Wolf, come boy! (*Shakes head.*) Has my faithful Wolf forgotten me, too? (*Again calling, louder.*) Here, Wolf, here, Wolf, come here, old friend! (*His loud calls attract a number of citizens who enter from both wings to surround him at a moderate distance. They examine him up and down, discuss him among themselves.*)

MAYOR (*striding authoritatively toward Rip Van Winkle*): Look here, my good fellow, you cannot disturb the peace and quiet with all this shouting. As mayor of this village I'd like to know who you are and what you want.

RIP VAN WINKLE (*confused*): You want to know who I am? Please, sir, don't you recognize me?

MAYOR: Well, now, we recognize only an old fellow with a gray beard. Tell us who you are and why you have caused such an uproar. We have no time for loafers, sir; you may be sure of that. (*Rip, more confused than ever, hesitates.*) Come, Mr. Graybeard, speak up!

FIRST CITIZEN (*as he examines Rip Van Winkle's old rifle*): I think it most likely that he is a soldier of King George of England. (*Nodding vigorously.*) That's who he is—an enemy spy! (*The crowd angrily repeats the word* Spy.)

SECOND CITIZEN (*laughing at Rip Van Winkle*): A spy? Ha! Come, old man, don't you know the war is over? If you are a spy you are a bit too late to do King George any good. (*The crowd chuckles at the joke.*)

RIP VAN WINKLE (*searching faces in the crowd*): Mr. Vedder

. . . Nicholas Vedder . . . are you here? (*To crowd.*) Mr. Vedder will tell you that I am no English spy.

THIRD CITIZEN: Mr. Vedder has been gone from us these last eighteen years. Don't tell us that you and the good Nicholas Vedder were friends?

RIP VAN WINKLE (*searching faces of other citizens who now enter from both wings*): Where is Brom Dutcher? Many days we spent together hunting in the Catskills. Brom Dutcher, here is your old friend.

FOURTH CITIZEN: Brom Dutcher no longer hunts for squirrels. Some say he was a hero at the battle of Stony Point. Others say he was lost in a storm. No one knows—he never came back. That was a long, long time ago, old man.

RIP VAN WINKLE: Maybe . . . maybe Derrick Van Bummel, the schoolmaster, can help me. (*As his distress deepens he pauses, sighs and again searches the crowd.*) Can you tell me where I can find him?

FIFTH CITIZEN (*as crowd shakes heads, muttering*): We have no schoolmaster by that name. (*Nods as he remembers.*) Come to think of it, there used to be a fellow who called himself Van Bummel. He, too, marched off to war. I've been told he got elected to Congress. At any rate, you're not likely to find him among us any more.

MAYOR (*sternly*): Enough of this! Tell us your name, old fellow . . . that is, if you have one.

RIP VAN WINKLE: My name, sir? (*Sighing.*) I was hoping that one of you would call me by name. Please, friends, my name is . . . Rip Van Winkle. (*Citizens shrug, repeat his name, shake heads as if his name is unfamiliar.*)

SIXTH CITIZEN, Rip Van Winkle, you say? And why might Rip Van Winkle ask so many questions about us? No one seems to know you, and you seem to know no one. (*Chuckles, winks at crowd.*) I think our old fellow has mistaken us for some of his mountain squirrels. (*The crowd chuckles.*)

RIP VAN WINKLE (*looks offstage right, where his former home was located, walks expectantly toward it.*) My home . . . there! Here is where I live. (*He stands at stage right, staring into wing; he calls.*) Good wife! Dame Van Winkle, are you here? Good wife, your husband has returned. . . . (*He droops as he sees that his home is vacant.*) All is empty . . . quiet. Dame Van Winkle has gone . . . and my children.

SEVENTH CITIZEN: If memory serves me rightly, I do remember something of a Dame Van Winkle. She used to keep an enormous tea kettle in her window. Proud she was of that immense tea kettle.

EIGHTH CITIZEN (*shaking head*): No, no, you are mistaken. You are probably thinking of Dame Van Horn who owned an enormous yellow cow. It used to wander into my potato patch at least twice a week.

NINTH CITIZEN (*shaking head, gesturing to right wing*): I am afraid both of you are wrong. This humble home was occupied by the preacher Peter Hudson. How well I remember his fiery sermons on the Sabbath day.

MAYOR (*holds up arms for silence, addresses Rip Van Winkle*): You claim to be our neighbor, Mr.—what do you call yourself —Mr. Rip Van Winkle? (*Addressing crowd.*) Fellow citizens, is Mr. Graybeard Van Winkle your neighbor? (*Crowd shouts* No.) Does he speak the truth when he says he lives in our village? (*Crowd shouts* No.) Have we ever set eyes upon him before? (*Crowd shouts* No *and* Never.)

TENTH CITIZEN: That should be enough to take care of you, Mr. Graybeard Van Winkle. Suppose you take yourself and your fanciful stories back to your cave in the mountain. I think you will be far more at home among a village of wild squirrels! (*Crowd nods agreement, chuckles.*)

RIP VAN WINKLE (*sighing*): Friends, please let me tell you a strange story . . . a story so peculiar that I must confess that I hardly believe it myself. (*Crowd grows quiet and attentive.*) It must have been twenty years ago that I set out to the Catskills with my faithful dog, Wolf. After bagging a few squirrels and pigeons I started back to my good wife and my warm fireside. As I was about to descend the mountain I heard a strange voice calling my name. I asked myself, who could be calling for Rip Van Winkle upon this lonely mountaintop? Upon turning around I saw an odd little creature who barely resembled a man. He was a short, square-built old fellow with thick, bushy hair and a grizzled beard. When I asked him why he called my name, he motioned for me to follow him. I was so amazed by his fantastic appearance that I went along with him until we reached a flat valley. Here I sighted many more of these fanciful creatures who were playing a game of tenpins. The roar of the balls as they crashed against the pins echoed like great peals of thunder. . . .

FIRST CITIZEN (*scoffing*): Come, come, your imagination has taken flight indeed. Little men who bowl at tenpins! Ha! (*Crowd laughs.*)

SECOND CITIZEN (*holding up arms for silence*): No, no, let us hear him out. Go on with your adventurous tale, Mr. Van Winkle. (*The crowd grows quiet.*)

RIP VAN WINKLE: My little companions then invited me to

join in their festivities, which I did. But I must confess that I was not used to such violent activity, so I soon grew drowsy. Finally, I could stay awake no longer. I fell into a deep, overpowering sleep.

THIRD CITIZEN (*as all eagerly listen*): And then what happened?

RIP VAN WINKLE: When at last I woke up I looked around for my strange companions. But they had disappeared. The tenpins were nowhere to be seen. All was silent. The grass had overgrown everything around me, my rifle was covered with rust, my faithful hound had disappeared. (*Pauses briefly, gestures.*) Call it my dream or call it my fanciful imagination, but that is what happened to me.

FOURTH CITIZEN (*in amazement*): Twenty years ago. . . .

FIFTH CITIZEN: You mean that you actually slept for twenty long years? (*Rip nods.*)

SIXTH CITIZEN (*addresses crowd*): Well, fellow citizens, what do we think of this fellow's strange tale? (*Crowd is of mixed opinions, mutters in confusion.*)

SEVENTH CITIZEN (*boldly*): A fanciful tale indeed! I, for one, do not believe a word of it!

RIP VAN WINKLE (*wearily*): It is all right, good neighbors. You don't believe me, and I cannot blame you. Perhaps you are right . . . maybe I belong (*gestures toward left wing*) out there. (*He sighs, slowly turns toward left stage. He suddenly catches sight of a young lady, peers closely, exclaims as he approaches her.*) Young lady . . . your face . . . I know who you are. Yes, you are my daughter; I am your father. Young Rip Van Winkle once—old Rip Van Winkle now! (*As the puzzled girl hesitates, Rip looks desperately around once more.*) Does nobody recognize old Rip Van Winkle? No? (*He droops, falters toward left wing.*)

OLD WOMAN (*totters out from crowd, shades her brow with palm, peers closely at Rip's face*): Somewhere I have seen those eyes before. . . . (*She gestures toward the Old Man who also approaches.*) My good husband, do you remember a fellow like this who used to bring us berries and nuts from the hillside? Remember how he would urge us to fill our baskets? A generous soul he was.

OLD MAN (*studies Rip*): Yes, I do remember such a happy sort of fellow who used to wander about doing whatever he pleased. He always had a fine hound at his heels. Yes, his dog's name was Wolf all right.

OLD WOMAN (*brightly*): Sure enough! It is Rip Van Winkle. Yes, yes, we know you, sir! (*Gently pats Rip Van Winkle's arm.*) Welcome home, old neighbor! (*Rip bursts into smiles.*)

MAYOR (*as crowd cheers, gathers closer to Rip*): Welcome home, friend and neighbor! (*Crowd joins a little bashfully in the welcome.*)

EIGHTH CITIZEN (*taking Rip's arm*): Welcome! Come, sir, we want to hear more of your adventure! (*Crowd opens the way as the Eighth Citizen escorts Rip to bench at upstage center. He sits, surrounded by citizens; his daughter stands at his side.*)

NINTH CITIZEN (*shouting*): We believe Rip's story—and we hope it will be told as long as there are stories to tell! We want strangers who pass through our village to hear of the twenty years' sleep of Rip Van Winkle.

TENTH CITIZEN (*shouting*): It shall be heard all over the world!

MAYOR: The fantastic adventures of Mr. Rip Van Winkle! . . . did he dream them or did he live them? It makes no difference. He is not only our friend and neighbor—but he is also a legend who will live forever! (*Mayor and crowd turn to Rip.*) Rip Van Winkle—a legend forever! (*Curtain falls.*)

THE STRANGE TALE
OF KING MIDAS

CHARACTERS

Narrator	Second Princess
King Midas	Third Princess
First Servant	First Prince
Second Servant	Second Prince
The Weary Traveller	Third Prince
Bacchus	Extra Court Members
First Princess	

INTRODUCTION BY NARRATOR

Ladies and gentlemen, welcome! We believe we have a treat for you this evening. Our class will act out for you one of the most famous of the ancient Greek myths. Perhaps you have read the strange story of King Midas who ruled the kingdom of Phrygia . . . tonight you will *see* his story. Our dramatic presentation is entitled "The Strange Tale of King Midas."

There was one thing in life which King Midas treasured above everything else. This one thing was an obsession with him; he craved it more and more . . . but I had better not give away the story! (*Narrator exits. Curtain rises.*)

SETTING AT RISE OF CURTAIN

The scene is a royal room in the king's palace. Suitable furniture is set in background. King Midas is seated upon his throne at upstage center. On a low table before him is a large box labelled "Treasure." The box is filled with a variety of riches, such as necklaces, rings, bracelets, gold and silver cups. King Midas eagerly holds them up, admires them.

KING MIDAS: Gold! Silver! Precious stones sparkling with light! They are mine, all mine! I am the richest king in all the kingdoms of the world. (*Clapping his hands.*) Hasten, royal servants! (*First Servant quickly enters.*)

FIRST SERVANT (*bowing deeply*): Yes, O royal king?

KING MIDAS (*gesturing nervously*): Gold, more gold! Fetch me another royal treasure chest. Quickly!

FIRST SERVANT: At once, your majesty. (*First Servant backs away while bowing, exits.*)

SECOND SERVANT (*entering, bowing*): O great King Midas, there is a weary traveller at the palace gate who begs for food and rest. Shall I send him on his way?

KING MIDAS (*somewhat annoyed*): Can't you see that I am counting my gold? (*Shrugging impatiently.*) Ah, well, send him to me. (*Second Servant bows and exits as King Midas greedily continues to enjoy his treasure.*)

(*The Weary Traveller enters, falls on his knees before King Midas.*)

WEARY TRAVELLER (*gratefully*): May all good things come to you, O kindly king. I beseech but a dry crust of bread and a stone upon which to lay my weary head.

(*First and Second Servants enter with a heavy box labelled "Gold." They set it on the table before King Midas.*)

KING MIDAS (*ignoring the Weary Traveller as he greedily digs both hands into gold coins and other golden objects*): My precious gold! How it warms my hands! I shall spend the rest of the day counting my golden treasures! (*Greedily chuckling.*) Ha-ha-ha!

FIRST SERVANT (*coughing, to attract the king's attention*): A-hum . . . a-hum!

KING MIDAS (*looking up in annoyance*): Yes, yes, what is it?

FIRST SERVANT (*gesturing to the kneeling Weary Traveller*): Pardon, your majesty, but. . . .

KING MIDAS (*sighing*): Oh, yes. (*Briskly, but with kindness.*) Take this weary fellow to the royal dining hall. Give him everything he needs. (*He again fondles his gold.*)

WEARY TRAVELLER (*backing away, bowing with upraised arms*): The blessing of heaven upon your kindly majesty. Great praise to noble King Midas.

(*King Midas ignores the Weary Traveller and the servants as they exit. He greedily ad libs as he lets his treasures slip from his fingers to fall back into the chest. Bacchus, who wears bright garments and a wreath on his head, steps onstage at right and silently faces King Midas. Bacchus is more or less hidden from King Midas—by a stage property—but is clearly visible to audience.*)

KING MIDAS (*slowly looking up and around in suspicion*): I sense a stranger . . . who is there? (*Standing, he angrily jerks his head about.*) Who dares to enter the royal chambers without permission?

BACCHUS (*approaching King Midas slowly and with great dignity*): I am no stranger to you, King Midas.

KING MIDAS (*in astonishment*): Bacchus! One of the gods come down from Mount Olympus! (*Bowing.*) I am honored by the presence of mighty Bacchus!

BACCHUS: I have observed your mercy and kindness to the weary traveller. That needy man was Silenus, my foster-father. Because you have shown him compassion, I will grant you your fondest wish. Whatever you ask I will grant immediately.

KING MIDAS (*tilting head, thinking deeply*): My fondest wish!

Hmmm. What shall I choose? Hmmm. (*Exclaiming, suddenly.*) I know. Please, great Bacchus, I wish that everything I touch should turn to gold! I wish to have the golden touch.

BACCHUS (*solemnly*): I do not approve of your wish, King Midas, but it is hereby granted. (*Raising arms toward King Midas.*) Henceforth, everything you touch shall turn instantly to gold! (*Lowering arms.*) I leave you with your golden touch. (*Bacchus exits.*)

KING MIDAS (*jubilantly holding up and admiring his hands*): My golden touch! (*Eagerly.*) I must test it! (*He touches an apple in a fruit basket, holds up a golden apple.*) A golden apple! (*Racing to a potted plant he plucks off a twig, holds it up.*) Gold, gold, pure gold! (Note: *The apple and twig, which are covered with gold-colored paper, should be originally placed out of sight of the audience, so that when held up they will appear to have turned to gold. King Midas now calls excitedly into both wings, gestures inward.*) Come, lords and ladies of the royal court! Witness the magic of King Midas! (*The three Princesses and three Princes, plus Extras, quickly enter from both wings. They bow.*)

FIRST PRINCESS: We await your majesty's pleasure.

KING MIDAS (*shouting*): Then behold, as my royal chambers turn to pure gold! (*He races to two or three small objects, holding them up while ad libbing:* Gold! . . . Look! . . . The golden touch! *The others gasp in astonishment while also ad libbing:* Amazing! . . . How can this be? . . . Look, it turned to gold!)

FIRST PRINCE: Congratulations, O king! Your fame will spread to the far corners of the earth! (*The two servants enter with trays loaded with fruits, vegetables, cakes.*)

FIRST SERVANT (*bowing*): The royal dinner hour, your majesty.

KING MIDAS (*annoyed by the interruption*): What's that? . . . oh, yes. Set them down and be off with you. (*The servants set trays on a table and exit.*) Come, royal lords and ladies; we must

celebrate my good fortune. (*The Princes and Princesses gather around the trays, while King Midas lingers, still admiring his gold.*)

SECOND PRINCESS (*biting a small cake, nodding appreciatively*): The baker has outdone himself with his sweetcakes. (*To King Midas.*) Come, your majesty, the royal dinner awaits. (*As King Midas approaches, the Second Prince hands him a small cake.*)

SECOND PRINCE: Try this tasty sweetcake.

KING MIDAS (*grimacing as he tastes*): What kind of a joke is this? (*Staring in horror at cake.*) A cake of gold! (*He tosses the cake aside, quickly reaches for a grape, fearfully stares, tosses it aside while groaning.* Note: *the cake and the grape are also previously wrapped in gold-colored paper. As King Midas first takes them he covers them with his hand so that they cannot be seen by the audience. Then, as he holds them up in horror, the audience sees that they are golden. King Midas shouts in terror.*) My dinner itself has turned into gold!

THIRD PRINCESS (*sympathetically*): Poor, poor King Midas. Everything you touch turns into hard, cold metal. What shall you do for your dinner? (*King Midas dismally shakes his head, walks droopily to his throne, sits and leans forward with head cupped in hands.*)

THIRD PRINCE (*to others*): We must help our king.

FIRST PRINCESS (*gesturing hopelessly*): But how?

FIRST PRINCE: Yes, how can we help him? He cannot eat his gold, neither can he drink it.

SECOND PRINCESS: Nor can he ride throughout his kingdom upon a golden horse.

SECOND PRINCE (*as all gaze sympathetically at the dejected King Midas*): It was a sorry hour that our king acquired the golden touch. (*Gesturing.*) Come, let us leave him to his sorrow. Perhaps we can devise some magic which will relieve him of his curse. (*All except King Midas exit.*)

KING MIDAS (*standing, after a brief pause, pleading as he sadly looks around*): Bacchus, god of Mount Olympus, hear my humble prayer. I beseech you to take away my grief. (*Nodding.*) I have been a greedy man. (*Closing his eyes, he bows his head.*)

BACCHUS (*entering, holding upraised hands over King Midas*): Because you repent of your greed, I take pity upon you. (*King Midas hopefully raises his head.*) Go to the River Pactolus and plunge yourself into its cleansing waters. Do this and you will be healed of your golden touch. And may you always remember that there are far more precious treasures in life than gold. (*Bacchus exits. The Princesses and Princes enter.*)

THIRD PRINCESS (*glancing about*): We heard a strange voice, your majesty. . . . (*Brightly, as she sees the joy on the face of King Midas.*) Your majesty . . . your face is bright with joy . . . what has happened?

KING MIDAS (*nodding gratefully as he descends from throne*): My golden curse will vanish as I bathe in the waters of the River Pactolus. Come, lords and ladies, this is a happy day for all of us. Your king has lost his golden touch . . . but has won a great deal of wisdom.

THIRD PRINCE (*as all start to leave*): We rejoice with you, King Midas. Hail to our king, who is rich in peace and honor. (*Others bow to King Midas who then leads them offstage. Curtain falls.*)

AROUND THE WORLD —BY WAY OF AMERICA

CHARACTERS

Narrator	Mrs. Grant
Phileas Fogg	Mr. Grant
Passepartout	Mr. Fix
Aouda	Captain Smith
Train Conductor	Station Master
First Child	Mr. Mudge
Second Child	Indians
Third Child	Extra Passengers

INTRODUCTION BY NARRATOR

Ladies and gentlemen, you are about to see a two-act drama entitled "Around the World—by Way of America." Our play is taken from a portion of the classic book *Around the World in Eighty Days*, a great adventure story written by the French novelist, Jules Verne.

Our principal character is Phileas Fogg, an Englishman with a sense of daring. One evening Mr. Fogg attended a meeting of the Reform Club in London. There he told his fellow club members that he believed it was possible to travel around the world in eighty days. His friends thought he was joking—for at that period of history the only means of transportation were horses, sailing ships and slow locomotives.

But Mr. Fogg was not joking. He insisted that he could circle the world in eighty days. When his friends challenged him to prove it, Phileas Fogg left London that very night to begin his perilous journey. He was accompanied by his French servant, Passepartout.

Tonight's play includes two other principal characters. One of them is Mr. Fix, a detective who believes that Mr. Fogg is a fleeing criminal and follows him wherever he goes. Another character is Aouda, a young lady who was saved from tragedy in India by Mr. Fogg and his servant.

Our story opens as Mr. Fogg and his companions reach the western prairies of the United States—almost the last lap of their trip—and time is running out. They are on board a train headed for New York. So here we go—around the world! (*Narrator exits. Curtain rises.*)

ACT I
SETTING AT RISE OF CURTAIN

The scene is a railway lounge car. To give the actors enough room for movement—while maintaining the appearance of a train—the stage is set as follows: The car runs lengthwise from right stage to left stage, with the front of the car at the left. A row of passenger chairs is set along the back curtain, facing left stage. The rest of the car contains lounge-car equipment, such as a bookcase and a table set with food and drink. From time to time during the action, a bell, whistle or other offstage sounds typical of a train may be used.

Mr. and Mrs. Grant—plus Extra Passengers if desired—are quietly sitting on upstage chairs. Phileas Fogg and Passepartout sit at a small table at stage center.

MR. FOGG (*holding up a map to Passepartout*): Look, Passepartout, we are exactly on schedule. The prairies will be behind us within a few more hours—if all goes well.

PASSEPARTOUT (*nodding at map*): We should make it to the port of New York in plenty of time. And then for a fast ship back to London!

MR. FOGG (*lowering map*): I shall ever be grateful to you, Passepartout. Never did a man have a more faithful friend and servant. Wherever we have struggled—India, China, the Pacific Ocean—you have been my extra strength.

PASSEPARTOUT (*smiling*): The adventure itself is reward enough for me. Just think—the first men to circle the globe in eighty days!

(*Aouda, dressed in East Indian costume, enters from right.*)

MR. FOGG: Ah, Aouda, what do you think of this strange land? Is it far different from your native India?

AOUDA (*glancing and gesturing over heads of audience*): Very different, truly. Wherever I look I can see nothing but flat prairies and rolling hills. I haven't seen a single human being out there all morning. . . . (*Anxiously.*) Except for those feathered savages charging about on their wild ponies. Are we in danger?

PASSEPARTOUT: Bows and arrows are always dangerous. The savages are American Indians—called the Sioux tribe.

AOUDA: I shall try not to be frightened. (*Conductor enters from left.*)

MR. FOGG: Conductor, please, are we on time?

CONDUCTOR (*glancing at watch, gesturing toward left wing*): The engineer says we'll make it to Omaha on schedule unless snow blocks the track. But we shouldn't have much trouble with the weather.

AOUDA (*anxiously gesturing*): What about the Indians? They seem to be following us.

CONDUCTOR: The Sioux is a warlike tribe, miss, but I wouldn't worry. We're not far from the army garrison at Fort Kearny.

(*Aouda sits at table with Mr. Fogg and Passepartout. The three children noisily race in from right. They ad lib:* Run, run . . .The redskins are coming! . . . Watch out for the Indians! *The conductor grins, speaks to Aouda.*) You see, our children are more terrifying than our Indians. (*Speaking playfully to the children.*) That's enough war-whoops for my train. (*Gesturing toward upstage passengers.*) Maybe they have some cakes for you over there. (*Conductor exits.*)

FIRST CHILD (*curiously wandering to Mr. Fogg*): You don't look like an Indian. Are you an Indian in disguise?

MR. FOGG (*chuckling in amusement*): No indeed, little friend. I am what you call an Englishman.

SECOND CHILD (*puzzledly*): What's an . . . an Englishman?

THIRD CHILD (*innocently, to second child*): Maybe an Englishman is a savage without feathers. (*The adults chuckle in amusement.*)

MRS. GRANT (*calling*): Children! Come here!

MR. GRANT (*calling apologetically to Mr. Fogg*): Sorry, sir; they have Indians on their minds.

FIRST CHILD (*to Passepartout*): We're going to Chicago. Where are you going?

PASSEPARTOUT: Our home is in London.

SECOND CHILD (*gesturing toward right wing*): The man in the next car said something about London. (*Frowning.*) That's funny, but he said that you folks might never get there.

MR. FOGG (*tilting his head curiously*): You heard a man say that? What did he look like?

THIRD CHILD (*shrugging*): Well, he didn't look like an Indian. I guess he looked more like . . . like what you call an Englishman.

AOUDA (*sighing*): It's our detective friend, Mr. Fix. He's still with us.

MRS. GRANT (*calling to children*): Children, come over here. We'll play a quiet game for a while. (*The children join their parents upstage where they sit and play silently.*)

AOUDA (*to Mr. Fogg*): What a terrible injustice that you should be hounded halfway around the world by that Mr. Fix. What does he want with you?

MR. FIX (*entering from right*): Mr. Fix himself can give you an answer. (*Indicating vacant chair at table.*) May I?

MR. FOGG : As you wish. (*Mr. Fix sits.*)

MR. FIX (*to Mr. Fogg, somewhat apologetically*): As I've told you before, sir, I'm only doing my duty. A bank was robbed just before you left London in such a hurry. You'll admit, sir, it looks suspicious. What do you say to that?

MR. FOGG (*shrugging*): I doubt if your suspicious mind would accept my explanation. If it is your duty to follow me around the world, I have no objection—but I must warn you against arresting an innocent man. I assure you that I shall soon return to London. Why not hold off until we both return home?

MR. FIX: It's part of my job to have a suspicious mind, Mr. Fogg. For all I know you may not be planning to return to England. That's why I'm sticking close.

PASSEPARTOUT: All we ask is that you do not delay our journey. Mr. Fogg cannot afford to waste hours, or even minutes. (*Indians suddenly shriek offstage.*)

MRS. GRANT (*rising, screaming, gathering her children*): It's the Indians! They're here! (*All players leap up, startled.*)

MR. FOGG (*taking command, gesturing toward left wing*): Throw up a barricade. Hurry! (*All rush about, shouting, piling boxes near left wing. If Extra Passengers are used, they immediately rush offstage at right.*)

PASSEPARTOUT (*to the Grants*): Let's get the children away! (*The Grants and Passepartout hustle the children toward the right, while ad libbing:* Run! . . . Hurry! . . . Over there! *Just as they are about to exit at right Indians—three or more—dash in from right to grab Passepartout and Mr. and Mrs. Grant. The children scream, elude the Indians, race over to safety at the left where the others still are. Mr. Fogg and Mr. Fix grab clubs and start to dash toward right, just as the Indians drag their three prisoners offstage.*)

CONDUCTOR (*entering, climbing around barricade of boxes, shouting to Mr. Fogg and Mr. Fix*): Come back! It's hopeless! The train's surrounded.

MR. FOGG (*as he and Mr. Fix reluctantly halt*): But we've got to do something!

AOUDA (*comforting the children who cling whimperingly to her*):

There, there; everything will turn out all right. Come with me. (*She takes the children offstage at left.*)

MR. FOGG (*agitated*): My old friend Passepartout . . . and the Grants . . . taken by those savages. (*Firmly.*) Gentlemen, we've got to go after them.

CONDUCTOR (*shaking head*): You don't realize what we're up against. (*Gesturing.*) Come here. (*Conductor leads others to a downstage position where he gestures outward toward audience.*) Look out the window. They're across the river already. Only a miracle can save them. (*Offstage hoofbeats sound.*)

MR. FIX (*tilting head*): I hear hoofbeats. (*Tensely.*) Another attack?

CONDUCTOR (*looking out*): We're all right. It's the troops from Fort Kearny—at least fifty men. But too late to save the others, I'm afraid. (*Gesturing toward left wing.*) Here comes Captain Smith.

CAPTAIN SMITH (*striding onstage, glancing around*): Any wounded?

MR. FIX: We're all right. But three passengers were taken.

MR. FOGG (*to Captain Smith*): Your men must ride at once! Perhaps there is time.

CAPTAIN SMITH (*shaking head*): About one chance in a million.

MR. FOGG (*insisting*): Then you must take that chance!

CAPTAIN SMITH (*politely but firmly*): I can't risk the lives of fifty men on the bare hope of saving three. You don't know the tricks the Sioux have—perhaps an ambush is already set for us. Believe me, sir, if anything could be done I would do it.

MR. FOGG (*with determination*): Very well. I will go alone.

MR. FIX: Be reasonable, Fogg. If it's hopeless for the army, it's doubly useless for you.

CONDUCTOR: He's right. They'd pick you off the minute you hit their hills.

MR. FOGG: My mind is made up. Captain, I want to borrow a horse.

CAPTAIN SMITH (*giving in*): All right, if you want to give it a try I'll give you a horse and five of my best men. But you'll only find out how impossible it is. Come along. (*Captain Smith and Mr. Fogg exit at left. Mr. Fix and Conductor watch them leave.*)

MR. FIX: A brave fellow, that Phileas Fogg.

CONDUCTOR (*nodding in admiration*): We could use more of his kind of courage.

MR. FIX (*reflectively*): I wonder if I'm wrong about him? He doesn't seem to be a criminal.

CONDUCTOR: A few minutes ago his only goal was to get to New York quickly. Now he's sacrificing hours and days—perhaps even his life.

MR. FIX (*nodding toward left*): Yes, maybe I've made a mistake. (*After a brief pause he suddenly gestures, speaks briskly.*) Come along; perhaps the others need help. (*They exit. Curtain falls.*)

INTRODUCTION BY NARRATOR TO ACT II

Phileas Fogg wanted to go around the world in eighty days, but at this point it looks more like *one hundred* and eighty. There are so many hazards . . . he may be captured by the Indians . . . perhaps he'll get lost on the prairie. London—and the completion of the journey—is still a long way off. But perhaps things will take a turn for the better. Act II takes place several hours later at a prairie railway station. Let's see how things turn out. (*Narrator exits. Curtain rises.*)

ACT II
SETTING AT RISE OF CURTAIN

The railway station is indicated by a sign reading *Fort Kearny Station*. Typical items, such as luggage and benches, are set in the background.

If Extra Passengers are used, they sit or stand at various upstage positions. The Station Master is making notes in his book.

AOUDA (*entering, anxiously approaching Station Master*): Is there any word of Mr. Fogg? (*Looking outward.*) Isn't there some way we can find out what's happening?

STATION MASTER (*shaking head*): It was a dangerous attempt, Miss. Your Mr. Fogg was brave enough, but. . . . (*He looks toward right as bell sounds.*) Here comes the next train. I suggest that you and the others make plans to leave on it. (*Sympathetically.*) Sorry, miss.

AOUDA (*shakily*): No, I can't leave . . . not until I know what has happened.

STATION MASTER: That could mean a long wait. (*Glancing toward right.*) Excuse me, miss; the train's pulling in. (*As the bell rings the Station Master calls out.*) All aboard for Omaha and points east! All aboard! (*The Station Master exits at right. Some of the Extra Passengers, if any, gather their belongings and follow the Station Master offstage.*)

MR. FIX (*racing in from left, shouting, gesturing toward right wing*): The troops are coming back!

AOUDA (*anxiously*): What about Mr. Fogg and the others?

MR. FIX: I don't know. They may be with the soldiers. Captain Smith will bring us word in a minute.

STATION MASTER (*entering, remaining at right wing, calling*): All aboard for Omaha! (*To Aouda and Mr. Fix.*) Last call, folks.

AOUDA (*to Mr. Fix*): Are you staying, too?

MR. FIX (*nodding*): I must find out what has happened to Mr. Fogg.

STATION MASTER: Coming, folks?

MR. FIX (*to Station Master*): Tell the engineer to go ahead. (*The Station Master waves toward right wing as if signalling the engineer. The bell rings several times as the Station Master resumes writing.*)

AOUDA (*gesturing toward left wing*): There goes the train.

MR. FIX (*gesturing excitedly toward right wing*): And here they come!

AOUDA (*eagerly, to Captain Smith who enters from right*): Are they all right? (*Looking toward right.*) Please, are they here? (*The Captain smiles, gesturing toward right wing. Mr. Fogg, Passepartout, and Mr. and Mrs. Grant enter. Aouda gasps in relief, hurries toward them.*)

MRS. GRANT (*anxiously*): Where are our children?

STATION MASTER: They're quite safe. I'll take you to them in a moment.

MR. FOGG (*briskly, breathlessly*): The train. We heard it from a distance. How soon will it arrive?

STATION MASTER: Sorry, sir, it has come and gone. You missed it by seconds.

AOUDA: But you are safe, Mr. Fogg; that's all that matters. What happened out there?

MR. FOGG: We battled the Indians ten miles south of here. They rode off after a short, hard fight. (*Anxiously.*) But I'm many hours behind schedule; I've got to make it up. (*To Station Master.*) When does the next train come?

STATION MASTER: Not until late this evening. (*To Mr. and Mrs. Grant.*) Come, I'll take you to your children. (*The Grants follow the Station Master offstage.*)

MR. FOGG (*desperately*): I've got to reach New York in time to catch the ship for London. (*Swinging around to Captain Smith.*) Captain, what about horses?

CAPTAIN SMITH: Too much ice on the ground between here and Omaha. Besides, the horses would tire after a few hours.

PASSEPARTOUT (*apologetically*): It's all my fault, sir. You wouldn't be here if I had been more careful.

MR. FOGG: Never mind, friend. Let's concentrate on our problem. (*Emphatically.*) There must be a way.

MR. FIX (*to Mr. Fogg*): Is it absolutely necessary for you to reach New York by the eleventh of this month?

MR. FOGG: Absolutely.

MR. FIX: Suppose I provided the way. Would you promise not to escape?

PASSEPARTOUT: Mr. Fogg has no wish to escape anywhere but to the east coast, and then home. You can be sure of that.

AOUDA: Why do you ask these questions, Mr. Fix?

MR. FIX (*to Mr. Fogg*): If I have your word, I believe I can help.

MR. FOGG (*impatiently*): You have my word, sir! Out with it!

MR. FIX: I had an idea you wouldn't be stopped by those Indians so I made plans to regain your lost time. At least we can try. (*Calling into wing.*) Mr. Mudge!

MR. MUDGE (*appearing at right wing*): All set, Mr. Fix? Shall I bring it out?

MR. FIX: At once. (*To Passepartout and Captain Smith as he gestures toward Mr. Mudge.*) Will you be so kind as to give Mr. Mudge a hand? (*Passepartout and Captain Smith follow Mr. Mudge offstage.*)

AOUDA (*curiously peering into wing*): What is it?

MR. FIX: You shall see. Ah, here it comes.

(*The three men push a low, wide sled onstage. The sled may be simply made by attaching wooden or cardboard runners to a wheeled wagon. By covering the wheels with overhanging canvas, the sled will appear to slide on the runners. The sled should look large enough for several persons. To achieve this, extend a cardboard platform over the sides and beyond the rear wheels. A sailing mast stands upright toward the front of the sled.*)

MR. FOGG (*staring, gasping*): What kind of a joke is this?

MR. FIX: No joke, I assure you. (*To Mr. Mudge.*) Mr. Mudge, please explain it.

MR. MUDGE (*enthusiastically*): Gentlemen, here is your per-

fect vehicle for speeding across the icy prairies. Believe me, you will win your race.

PASSEPARTOUT (*in bewilderment as he studies the sled*): You mean we are to push our way along? Or are we to be pulled by horses?

MR. MUDGE: Neither. Let me show you a power ten times that of a team of horses. (*Mr. Mudge picks up a sail from the sled, places it on the mast. The others gasp, mutter in appreciation. Mr. Mudge steps back, gesturing toward the sail.*) There you are! The power of the winter wind!

MR. FOGG (*enthusiastically*): A ship of the prairie! It just might work!

AOUDA: We can short-cut across the plains!

CAPTAIN SMITH (*nodding*): The winds may speed you into Omaha well ahead of the train itself.

MR. MUDGE: You should reach a speed of at least forty miles an hour. Keep yourself bundled up—the wind is as cold as it is mighty.

MR. FOGG (*triumphantly*): We'll win after all! (*Gesturing to Mr. Fix and Mr. Mudge.*) Thanks to you gentlemen.

CAPTAIN SMITH: You need have no fear of Indians. Should they sight your strange vehicle they'll ride for their lives.

MR. FIX (*chuckling*): What a sight that will be.

PASSEPARTOUT: We've journeyed by boat, train, ox-cart—even on elephant-back—but this is the strangest yet.

MR. MUDGE (*glancing at sky*): The wind is rising. Better sail with it.

MR. FOGG: Right! We have no time to lose. (*Getting onto sled, steering it.*) Give me enough start to catch the breeze. Once I'm started the rest of you can hop aboard. (*The others quickly toss small pieces of luggage onto the sled while happily ad libbing, such as:* We're on our way . . . Let's go . . . I'll push back here. *They push the sled so that it slowly rolls toward the left.*)

PASSEPARTOUT (*shouting, as they push*): Around the world!

MR. FOGG (*shouting triumphantly*): In eighty days! (*Guided by Mr. Fogg, the sled is pushed offstage. Passepartout, Aouda, and Mr. Fix chase offstage after it.*)

MR. MUDGE (*reflectively to Captain Smith, as they look toward left wing*): You know what I think, Captain Smith?

CAPTAIN SMITH: What, Mr. Mudge?

MR. MUDGE: I think they'll make it.

CAPTAIN SMITH: You know what I think?

MR. MUDGE: What?

CAPTAIN SMITH: I think you are absolutely right. (*Curtain falls.*)

Gulliver Wins His Freedom

CHARACTERS

Narrator	Army Captain
Gulliver	Prime Minister
First Lilliputian	Emperor
Second Lilliputian	First Prince
Third Lilliputian	First Princess
Fourth Lilliputian	Second Prince
Fifth Lilliputian	Second Princess
Sixth Lilliputian	Extras, Archers, Pages

INTRODUCTION BY NARRATOR

Good evening, ladies and gentlemen. We welcome you as our guests to a short drama in two acts. Our play is called "Gulliver Wins His Freedom." It is adapted from the classic *Gulliver's Travels*, by Jonathan Swift.

Our play takes place in the land of Lilliput. As you may remember, the Lilliputians were tiny folks, no larger than Gulliver's thumb. Although we searched for actors and actresses of thumb-size, we just couldn't find any! So you can help us out by imagining that our Lilliputian actors are just about six inches tall.

In the year 1699 Gulliver set sail from England with the

intention of voyaging to the South Seas. During a violent storm his ship was driven off course—and Gulliver was cast into the sea, near the coast of a strange little island. He managed to swim to shore, but was so exhausted by the effort that he immediately fell into a deep sleep. He was still sleeping the next morning . . . and here is where our story begins. (*Narrator exits. Curtain rises.*)

ACT I
SETTING AT RISE OF CURTAIN

The setting is the seashore. Gulliver is lying asleep at stage center, his head and feet toward the wings. *Note:* The smallness of the Lilliputians as compared to Gulliver can be emphasized in three ways: (a) By casting the tallest actor (wearing hat and boots) in the role of Gulliver. (b) By casting the smallest players as Lilliputians, and having them appear without hats, wearing low shoes or sandals. (c) By having Gulliver stay on an elevated area—such as a covered platform—so that it is necessary for the Lilliputians to look upward to him. His elevation also gives the audience a clear view of the reclining Gulliver.

The action begins as the First and Second Lilliputians enter with fishing poles. They suddenly notice Gulliver.

FIRST LILLIPUTIAN (*gasping with astonishment*): What is this? It appears to be some great monster from the sea! (*They cautiously edge closer.*) No! It's a human giant! See his enormous arms—like trees from the forest! (*Stage whispering.*) Shhhhh . . . he's asleep!

SECOND LILLIPUTIAN (*as they look with awe at Gulliver's great length:*) A Man Mountain indeed! (*In alarm.*) Why, this immense creature could clutch us between his very fingers! (*Gulliver rolls over heavily, groans loudly.*)

FIRST LILLIPUTIAN (*in terror*): He shakes the very earth with his groans!

SECOND LILLIPUTIAN (*beckoning*): Come, let us call out the army before he awakens. (*They hurriedly exit. Gulliver groans and rolls, but remains asleep. The following characters now enter: Army Captain; Prime Minister; Third, Fourth, Fifth and Sixth Lilliputians; a few Extras and Archers. They carry lengths of string, representing ropes. For a moment they are paralyzed at the sight of Gulliver.*

ARMY CAPTAIN (*giving commands in stage whisper*): Quickly, men! Bind him! Make sure of your knots! (*All except Prime Minister race silently, tossing and tying ropes around Gulliver who stirs and groans.*) Hurry! Faster! The Man Mountain awakens! (*As they complete their task the Army Captain waves his cardboard sword and shouts triumphantly.*) We have captured the Man Mountain! All cheer! (*The Lilliputians dance around Gulliver, shouting and cheering. Gulliver slowly awakens, tugs puzzledly at his ropes, lifts his head and stares dazedly around. As he suddenly understands that he is tied down he roars, struggles against the ropes, reaches with a free arm for the Lilliputians. They shriek in terror, retreat a few steps.*)

THIRD LILLIPUTIAN (*taunting Gulliver*): Tug and strain, O mighty giant, you shall not get free!

FOURTH LILLIPUTIAN (*boasting to others*): We Lilliputians are no larger than his thumb—yet he is our slave! (*Gulliver angrily roars, claws at Lilliputians who once more shriek and retreat.*)

GULLIVER (*who has moved his upper body enough to sit up on his elbow*): Tiny people, what harm have I done that you should bind me? I may be a giant to you, but I am not your enemy.

PRIME MINISTER (*stepping forward, shaking walking stick at Gulliver*): Silence! As the Prime Minister of his great and majestic emperor of Lilliput, I decree that you shall be carried to the gates of the royal palace. His royal highness shall decide your fate. (*The Prime Minister is a somewhat fumbling and comical character.*)

GULLIVER (*politely*): I shall be most pleased to meet your royal emperor, but. . . . (*Frowning.*) I have not eaten since yesterday. Surely you are a hospitable people who will not deny food and drink to a hungry visitor.

PRIME MINISTER (*doubtfully*): Hmmm . . . very well. (*To others.*) Fetch our unexpected guest some breakfast. (*A pair of Extras race offstage as the others make sure that Gulliver's ropes are secure. Gulliver again roars and clutches, somewhat playfully. The Lilliputians dance about him at a safe distance, laughing triumphantly. The Extras return with several small saucers containing bits of bread.*)

ARMY CAPTAIN (*raising sword to Gulliver*): Give us your word that we may serve you with safety.

GULLIVER (*nodding, licking lips*): Only let me taste your Lilliputian food. I am famished! (*The Lilliputians pass food to Gulliver who hungrily finishes within a few moments. He looks around, complainingly.*) But I have had but a bare morsel. Where is the breakfast you promised?

FIFTH LILLIPUTIAN (*in dismay*): He will eat our country clean. The giant has an appetite of . . . of . . . a giant.

ARMY CAPTAIN (*to Gulliver, gruffly*): Exactly what do you require?

GULLIVER (*cheerfully*): Suppose we start off with a dozen boiled eggs. . . . (*Frowning.*) Since they are Lilliputian eggs, better make it three dozen.

ARMY CAPTAIN (*sighing*): Three dozen eggs. What an omelet that will make. What else?

GULLIVER (*brightly*): Suppose we say six loaves of bread.

ARMY CAPTAIN (*sourly*): Suppose we say three loaves. Is that all? . . . I hope.

GULLIVER: I am very fond of fruit for breakfast.

ARMY CAPTAIN: Very well. We'll include a dozen grapes.

GULLIVER: Please . . . make that a dozen bunches of grapes.

(*Gulliver nods in satisfaction.*) That ought to give me a good start.

PRIME MINISTER (*sourly*): A start for you and the finish of us. (*To Lilliputians, impatiently.*) His royal majesty is anxious to see this gigantic fellow. Come, let us prepare to carry him to the palace.

GULLIVER (*amused*): Carry me? Ha! Why, I am fifty times the weight of all of you!

SIXTH LILLIPUTIAN: We are small in size but mighty in wisdom. (*Gesturing to others.*) Let us prove ourselves to the Man Mountain! (*The Army Captain and the Prime Minister ad lib orders to the others who rush offstage and return again with building materials, such as lumber, nails, hammers, wheels. Gulliver struggles and roars, but they ignore him as they go about their work. Curtain falls.*)

INTRODUCTION BY NARRATOR TO ACT II

The little Lilliputians were clever at that. They built an immense, flat platform which was made movable with dozens of tiny wheels. It wasn't easy to lift the Man Mountain, but with the aid of long, stout poles they managed to get him upon the rolling platform. Fifteen hundred tiny horses then hauled him to the gates of the Lilliputian city. There Gulliver was freed from his ropes, but he was chained by his left leg to a pillar.

The Man Mountain has mountains of problems all right. Let's find out whether he solves them. (*Narrator exits. Curtain rises.*)

ACT II
SETTING AT RISE OF CURTAIN

The scene is the city gates. Gulliver sits on a platform, surrounded by all the previous characters, plus new Extras. His left leg is chained (with cardboard links) to a pillar. Outdoor objects, such as small bushes and crockery, may be set in background. In order to maintain the appearance of great size Gulliver remains on his platform at all times.

GULLIVER (*complaining indignantly as the Lilliputians stare at him and discuss him among themselves*): What is this? Am I to be stared at like an elephant in a zoo? In my own land I am but one of thousands who are of my own size. You, my puny folks, are an amazing sight to me! I once owned a pet puppy who could have carried the lot of you upon his back! (*The Pages enter, blowing trumpets and beating drums.*)

PRIME MINISTER (*rapping his walking stick against the ground*): All hail! All hail his royal majesty, the emperor of Lilliput!

(*The Emperor majestically enters to the beat of the trumpets and drums. He is followed by the two princes and two princesses, plus other Extras if desired. All except Gulliver bow deeply and ad lib greetings to the Emperor. As the cheers die down, the Emperor walks about with great dignity, haughtily examining Gulliver.*)

EMPEROR (*shouting to Gulliver, as he suddenly remembers his own importance*): Where is your respect for royalty, Man Mountain? Bow to your emperor!

GULLIVER (*apologizing, though somewhat amused*): Forgive me, mighty king of Lilliput, but I was surprised that so great an emperor should be so tiny. (*Gulliver grins, bows from his sitting position several times with exaggerated courtesy.*) Hail to your great but small majesty!

EMPEROR (*sputtering indignantly*): For one in chains you are a saucy fellow. Take care that I do not turn my archers upon you.

GULLIVER (*respectfully*): Little king . . . I mean great king, I'd like to talk to you about my chains. (*Plucks chains.*) To put it frankly, I'd like them removed. (*Gestures.*) Surely I should be as free as the rest of your loyal subjects.

FIRST PRINCE (*objecting fearfully*): No, no, father; he must not be turned loose. Why, with his left hand alone he could sweep us all into the sea!

PRIME MINISTER (*to himself, weepingly*): And I'm such a poor swimmer. (*The crowd nods, muttering ad lib agreement to the First Prince's argument.*)

FIRST PRINCESS (*anxiously*): His enormous appetite could

bring famine to Lilliput. He requires six loaves of bread just to get warmed up for breakfast! (*The crowd again mutters agreement.*)

EMPEROR (*briskly, decisively*): Yes, yes, it is quite impossible. You must remain our prisoner.

PRIME MINISTER (*baffled*): Yet, what shall we do with him, your majesty? We have no ship great enough to send him on his way. What to do with him?

GULLIVER (*brightly*): I know what to do with him . . . I mean with me. It is true that I am as powerful as a hurricane . . . but this enormous strength can be of great service to you. Look! (*Gulliver slowly rises, stands with legs set somewhat apart, flexes his arms overhead. The Lilliputians gasp in awe, fall back.*)

ARMY CAPTAIN (*waving his sword toward Archers*): Watch out for treachery! (*The Archers crouch for action.*)

GULLIVER (*pleadingly*): Believe me, tiny folks, I want nothing more than liberty and peace. (*Gestures.*) Come close; let's talk as friends. (*Somewhat convinced of his good intentions, they cautiously draw closer. Gulliver smiles.*) That's better. (*He gestures toward a wing*) Now take your fields and orchards out there. I could gather and store your crops in less time than it takes to whistle a tune. (*Lilliputians nod as the idea appeals to them. Gulliver gestures toward other wing.*) I could also build you a great highway over the mountaintop. Think of the advantages of a broad, smooth road that reaches the opposite sea! (*Lilliputians nod even more approvingly; they ad lib enthusiastically. Gulliver flexes muscles.*) I am powerful, indeed, citizens of Lilliput. Why not let my strength work in your behalf?

EMPEROR (*gesturing for Prime Minister and Princes to approach him, then speaking to Gulliver*): Ahem . . . we will meet in grand council to discuss your proposals. (*Huddling, they ad lib and gesture as if considering the good and bad features of Gulliver's proposal.*)

GULLIVER (*cheerfully, as the discussion continues*): Don't forget—I make a much better friend than enemy!

ARMY CAPTAIN (*calling over to Emperor*): He has a good point there, your majesty.

EMPEROR (*to Lilliputians*): Loyal subjects, your royal emperor will hear your opinions on the matter. Let us consider the advantages and disadvantages of freeing the Man Mountain. Speak up!

FIRST LILLIPUTIAN (*happily*): Look at his mighty frame. The very sight of him would be enough to scare away our enemies!

SECOND LILLIPUTIAN (*shrugging glumly*): But the very sight of him also scares us.

THIRD LILLIPUTIAN (*cheerfully*): As he promised, he could pick our apple crops within an hour!

FOURTH LILLIPUTIAN (*sourly*): And gobble them up within the same hour.

FIFTH LILLIPUTIAN (*happily gestures skyward*): He could carry us across the sky! In his palm we could soar like birds!

SIXTH LILLIPUTIAN (*timidly*): But what if we fall? (*The Lilliputians gather in small groups to discuss the matter with animation. After talking briefly with the Emperor, the Prime Minister steps off to one side to scribble furiously on a long sheet of paper.*)

EMPEROR (*holding up hands to crowd*): Silence, loyal subjects. (*They quiet down. The Emperor addresses Gulliver.*) Ahem ... you are quite sure about all this business of harvesting our crops and building broad highways?

GULLIVER (*enthusiastically*): That would be just the beginning. I could even build a grand new palace for your majesty!

EMPEROR (*brightening*): A new palace . . . hmmm. (*Clears throat, speaks decisively to Lilliputians.*) I have come to my royal decision. The Man Mountain shall be set free. (*Shrugging.*) After all, you do want your imperial emperor to have a new palace. (*The crowd cheers in agreement.*)

GULLIVER (*happily*): I'd like to add my cheers. (*Waves arms.*) Three cheers for the emperor's wise decision!

EMPEROR (*gesturing to Prime Minister who is still scribbling*): Man Mountain, you will please notice that my Prime Minister is hard at work. (*To Prime Minister.*) Are you ready?

PRIME MINISTER (*dashing off final lines*): Coming! (*He approaches Gulliver, clears his throat.*) Giant visitor, attend to our royal decree. Your chains shall be loosened upon the following conditions. (*Again clearing his throat, he reads from the paper.*) First, you shall not depart from Lilliput without our permission.

GULLIVER: Agreed!

PRIME MINISTER (*reading*): Next, you shall not lie down in our fields of corn. (*Looks up.*) I guess you know why.

GULLIVER (*holding up palm in oath*): Not a stalk will I trample.

PRIME MINISTER (*reading*): While we will provide you with ample food and drink, you will please control your appetite.

SECOND PRINCE (*quickly*): In plainer language—no second helpings.

GULLIVER (*laughing*): Agreed, as long as the first servings are big enough.

PRIME MINISTER (*reading*): You shall assist our workmen as they beautify our country.

GULLIVER (*flexing muscles*): Agreed!

PRIME MINISTER (*pleased, as he folds paper*): You are a most agreeable fellow.

SECOND PRINCESS (*stage whispering to Prime Minister*): Don't forget the new palace . . . complete with a royal ballroom.

PRIME MINISTER (*reopening sheet*): Ah, yes . . . a new palace, complete with a royal ballroom. (*Folds paper.*)

GULLIVER: I agree to everything! (*Smiling, shrugging.*) As the Prime Minister said, I'm a pretty agreeable fellow, once you get to know me.

EMPEROR (*shouting*): Set him free! (*Several Lilliputians quickly unchain Gulliver. Gulliver rubs his ankle, waving gratefully. The Lilliputians dance around Gulliver, cheering and applauding him. If desired, background music may be added to the march-around. If used, Gulliver also claps time. The curtain falls on the celebration.*)

The Swiss Family Robinson —Rescued

CHARACTERS

Narrator	Jenny Montrose
Father Robinson	Captain Littlestone
Mother Robinson	Mr. Wolston
Fritz Robinson	Mrs. Wolston
Ernest Robinson	Mary Wolston
Jack Robinson	Martha Wolston
Franz Robinson	Extra Sailors

INTRODUCTION BY NARRATOR

Good evening, and welcome, ladies and gentlemen. Our actors and actresses are about to whisk you off to an island adventure. You will see a two-act drama adapted from the classic book written by Johann Wyss, *The Swiss Family Robinson*. Our dramatized portion of this book is called "The Swiss Family Robinson—Rescued."

Before the curtain rises, let's get acquainted with the Robinsons, a family that was shipwrecked on the island they call New Switzerland. The family consists of father and mother Robinson and their four sons—Fritz, Ernest, Jack and the youngest boy, Franz. What kind of folks are they? Well, the kind that makes an interesting story of adventure. The parents are courageous and resourceful—as we shall see. As for the boys, they are pretty much like . . . like normal, fun-loving boys—as we shall also see.

What a fascinating place New Switzerland was! It was rich with the natural beauties of forests, mountains, rivers and flower-scented meadows. As for the wildlife, the land swarmed with wild creatures of every sort, including elephants, ostriches, boa constrictors, lions and tigers.

Act I takes place several years after the Robinson family first found themselves on New Switzerland. They have brought some of their camping equipment—taken from the wrecked ship—down for a day at the seashore.

ACT I
SETTING AT RISE OF CURTAIN

The scene is the Robinson family's camping quarters by the shore. The sea is toward the left wing, inland is toward the right. Plant life is set along the background. General equipment, such as fishing poles, nets, boxes, cooking utensils, fruits and vegetables are in view. A small tent may be pitched at upstage right. Large rocks—made of cardboard—are set onstage near left wing.

Jack is sitting on a box with a basket of oysters (cardboard) in his lap. He takes the oysters, one at a time, pulls them apart, examines them, frowns and tosses them aside. Ernest enters with a coconut, peers curiously at Jack.

ERNEST (*approaching Jack*): What are you up to now, Jack? (*Looking into basket, laughing.*) Oh . . . more oysters.

JACK (*indignantly, as he continues to examine oysters*): Yes, more oysters, my dear brother Ernest. And someday I will have pearls. Just you wait.

ERNEST (*chuckling*): I've been waiting for years. So has mama. I doubt if you'll ever get her that pearl necklace. (*Holding coco-*

nut to lips.) But here's a real treasure. (*Drinking.*) Hmmm . . . delicious.

(*Father and Franz enter from left with baskets.*)

JACK: What do you have in there, Father? And you, Franz?

FATHER (*smiling, wagging finger*): When Franz and I go fishing we catch fish. (*To Franz.*) Let's set them over here. Mother will want to bake them for dinner. (*They set baskets off to one side. Father idly takes one of Jack's oysters, pulls it apart, shrugs, pats Jack's shoulder.*) Patience, son . . . maybe tomorrow. (*Looking around.*) Where's mother?

ERNEST (*gesturing toward left*): Waiting down at the boat landing. She's worried about Fritz. He's been gone five days now.

FRANZ (*scoffing*): No need to worry about him. He said he was going to sail along the north coast. I feel sorry for any sharks who get in his way.

FATHER: Come on, boys, we've had our day at the seaside. Time to bundle up and get home. (*The boys busy themselves by gathering up the equipment. Mother worriedly enters from left, Father approaches her, touches her cheek with his finger.*) Here, now, what's the meaning of this teardrop? (*With mock sternness.*) Just wait till that boy gets home . . . I'll teach him to wander off.

MOTHER (*worriedly*): It's not like Fritz to be gone so long. So many things could happen.

FATHER (*comforting her*): There, there . . . just let him catch a whiff of your marvelous fish dinner and he'll run all the way home. (*To boys.*) Have you been watching from the lookout station?

FRANZ (*nodding*): No sign of Fritz or of a rescue ship or anything else. I'll take another look tomorrow morning.

FATHER (*sighing, closing a box*): It's been a full day; suppose we get along home.

JACK (*quickly*): Wait a minute; I've got just three more to go in this batch. (*He eagerly breaks open the oysters, scowls, tosses them aside, sighs.*) Oh, well, the sea is full of oysters . . . and pearls, too, I hope. (*Franz wanders toward left with a telescope as the others gather equipment.*)

FRANZ: One last look. I wouldn't be surprised to see Fritz with a boatload of mermaids. (*He swings the telescope around, looking in various directions toward the left, suddenly halts, reacts with surprise.*) Wait! There is someone out there! In a canoe. Doesn't look like Fritz. (*Others race to left stage, Father takes telescope, peers.*)

FATHER: He's paddling toward us . . . appears to be a savage of some sort . . . a fierce-looking creature. (*Gesturing toward right wing.*) Get back! He may be a scout for a war tribe. (*All quickly retreat toward right wing while grabbing cardboard rifles and clubs.*)

MOTHER (*tensely*): He's coming . . . be careful. . . .

(*Fritz, in savage costume, stealthily creeps in from left, crouching behind the rocks. He peeps around the rocks at the others.*)

ERNEST (*taking a couple of steps forward, aiming his rifle*): Just one more step, Mister Savage, and I'll split you like a log.

MOTHER (*alarmed*): Ernest . . . no . . . stay back. (*Fritz continues to duck and peep.*)

FATHER: Perhaps he speaks our language. (*Calling with authority.*) You! Come out where we can see you! Out! (*Fritz pauses briefly, steps into full view with folded arms.*)

FRITZ (*grinning broadly*): So you want to see me. (*Holding arms out.*) How's that? See enough?

FRANZ (*exclaiming*): Fritz! You big ape!

MOTHER (*relieved, but reproving Fritz who advances*): Shame on you. Scaring us like that! Where have you been?

JACK (*grimly approaching Fritz*): I'll take care of this savage. (*Jack tries to shove a basket over Fritz's head, but Fritz laughs and nimbly dodges aside.*)

FATHER (*trying to be stern with Fritz*): You'll have lots of explaining to do when we get you home. (*Gesturing.*) But for now, grab a basket of fish and let's be on our way.

FRITZ (*shifting uncomfortably*): Father, mother . . . I can't leave just yet. You see. . . . (*Gesturing toward left.*) You see, while I was paddling around . . . I . . . uh. . . .

MOTHER (*anxiously*): What's the matter, son?

ERNEST (*as Fritz hesitates*): Out with it. What happened out there? Meet up with a prehistoric monster or something?

FRITZ (*still befuddled*): Not exactly a monster. As a matter of fact, it was something rather attractive. I mean. . . . (*Throwing up arms.*) I mean it's so unbelievable.

FATHER (*impatiently*): Just what do you mean?

FRITZ: It's a sort of surprise . . . at least a surprise to me. You see. . . . (*Shrugging, sighing.*) Instead of trying to tell you, maybe I'd better show you. (*Turning toward left.*) I'll be right back. (*He quickly exits at left.*)

FRANZ (*as all exchange baffled glances*): What do you suppose it is? I've never seen him act like this before.

JACK (*shrugging*): Maybe it's a mermaid after all. (*Fritz returns with Jenny in tow. The others gasp.*)

ERNEST (*exclaiming*): What . . . I mean who is this?

FRITZ: This is what I mean . . . I mean this is who I mean. (*To Jenny.*) Jenny, I'd like you to meet my mother and father— and my brothers. (*Grinning weakly, speaking to his family.*) My mother and my father and my brothers, please meet Jenny. Miss Jenny Montrose.

JACK (*rubbing his eyes in amazement*): But . . . but she's a girl.

FATHER (*smiling at Jack*): Such sharp eyes.

FRANZ (*to Jenny*): Are you a girl mermaid? I mean a mermaid kind of a girl? If you are, you're the prettiest thing I've ever seen come out of the sea.

MOTHER (*sharply*): Stop this nonsense! (*Holding out hand to Jenny.*) Come here, Jenny. Don't mind them. It's just that it's been so long since they've seen anything as lovely as you. Please tell us about yourself. Where did you meet Fritz?

ERNEST (*as he, Franz and Jack stare in wonderment at Jenny*): Think of it . . . a real, live girl.

FATHER (*nodding*): I guess dinner can wait. (*Beckoning.*) Come, Jenny. We'll feast on your story, instead. (*Jenny sits on a box at stage center. The others surround her.*)

JENNY: Years ago I lived in India with my father. He was a British officer. When he was recalled to England we took separate ships. My ship capsized in a storm, but I managed to make my way to shore. For three years I lived alone in the woods. Fritz was the first human being I had seen in three years. (*Gratefully.*) It's wonderful to be here.

MOTHER: What about your father?

JENNY (*doubtfully*): His ship probably reached England safely, but I don't know. Is there any way I can find out?

FRITZ (*shaking head*): This is the only world we have known for many years.

ERNEST (*trying to cheer up Jenny*): But it's an exciting life, Jenny. For instance, I can show you how to tame a wild monkey!

FRANZ (*eagerly*): And I'll help you to build your own tree house!

MOTHER (*smiling tolerantly at the boys*): That shows how little you boys know about a young lady like Jenny. It's a pretty new dress and a colored ribbon for her hair that she'll be wanting.

JENNY (*eagerly*): I'll make myself helpful to everyone. I can work in the kitchen and tend the garden . . . what fun it will be to share myself with friends again!

FATHER: Welcome to our family, Jenny. Your bright face will give additional strength to all of us. (*To Mother.*) Mother, why don't you show her around New Switzerland while we get our things back home? (*The boys load themselves with equipment as Mother escorts Jenny toward the right wing.*)

JACK (*calling*): Jenny, wait a minute! I may have a welcoming gift for you. (*Jack races to a basket of oysters, furiously breaks open two or three, scowls and tosses the shells aside. The others laugh.*) Just you wait, Miss Jenny Montrose; I'll find a pearl necklace for both you and mother. (*Scowling and gesturing toward basket.*) If those oysters would only cooperate. (*All chuckle once more and exit at right wing. Curtain falls.*)

INTRODUCTION BY NARRATOR TO ACT II

So a new and an interesting citizen has taken residence in the domain of New Switzerland. To the cry of the wind and the call of wild birds is added another sound—the pleasant voice of the lovely young lady named Jenny Montrose.

Time again passes as the Robinson family works, plays, and hopes for the day when a ship from the outer world will anchor off their island. As happy as they are, they wish for news of friends they used to know so long ago and await the time when they can let their old friends know they are alive and well.

One spring afternoon, after the day's work was done, they voted to take a stroll along the cool, refreshing beach. They enjoyed the seashore all the more because it offered them a view of the immense ocean—where a ship might be passing. Ladies and gentlemen, we present the second act of our drama.

ACT II
SETTING AT RISE OF CURTAIN

The seashore scene is somewhat similar to that of Act I. General camping equipment is set in background. The rocks used in Act I may be shifted to various upstage areas. Jenny is seated on a bench or box at stage center. Mother stands behind, combing Jenny's hair.

MOTHER: What lovely hair you have.

JENNY: Thanks to your expert grooming. (*Sighing.*) How I used to struggle with it when I was all alone. (*Three or four cannon roars sound. An offstage soundman can use a drum to represent the cannon. Jenny tilts her head toward right.*) What is that?

MOTHER: The men-folk are testing one of the cannons taken from our wrecked ship. We use it for long-distance signalling. Someday, perhaps, it may reach a passing ship.

JENNY: Mother, do you really think we'll ever be rescued? It's nice to hope, but maybe we're deceiving ourselves.

MOTHER: Hope is a great source of strength, Jenny, as long as you work with it.

JENNY: What do you mean by working with it?

MOTHER: By keeping busy, by making the best of things, by doing everything possible to make your hopes come true. I don't believe in the kind of hope that just sits around waiting for things to happen. Hope must be kept busy.

JENNY (*nodding*): That's why you folks have built such a rich life for yourself on this island. You hoped while working. (*In silence for a few moments, Mother continues with Jenny's hair. Father enters from right.*)

FATHER (*admiring Jenny*): As pretty as a poppy! No wonder the boys race back from their hunting trips. (*Cannon again sounds.*)

FRITZ (*entering from right, holding a fur over his head, growling*): Grrrrr . . . grrrrr . . . (*peeking through opening in fur.*) Surprise, Jenny! This will make a jacket—a fine fur for a fine lady. (*Stretching.*) Now, if you don't mind, I'll take my afternoon snooze. (*Lying down on back, raising head somewhat.*) Wake me in time for supper!

JENNY (*scolding playfully*): Lazybones! (*Ernest and Jack enter from right.*)

ERNEST (*scowling, wiping hands on a rag*): Keeping the rust off that old gun is a day's work in itself. (*Poking a foot at the dozing Fritz.*) As if you need to rest.

JACK: I'm the only one around here who doesn't take time off. I've got to work all the time.

JENNY: Doing what?

JACK (*grinning*): Doing this. (*Taking a basket, he again breaks open oysters. The cannon roars louder than before.*)

FATHER (*curiously*): Who's firing the gun?

MOTHER (*counting the others with her finger*): Fritz, Ernest, Jack, Papa . . . all here except Franz.

FRANZ (*entering from left*): Someone call Franz? Here I am, as handsome as ever. (*As the others exchange startled glances, Franz looks puzzled.*) What's the matter?

ERNEST: Did you come from the cannon?

FRANZ: Not me. I've been swimming in the bay.

FATHER (*with puzzled expression*): Must have been thunder.

JENNY (*glancing at sky*): On a clear day like this? (*As cannon again roars they mutter and exchange startled glances.*) There it is again!

FRITZ (*jumping to his feet*): A ship! It must be a ship! (*All race to various positions near left stage, peer excitedly into wing.*)

ERNEST: Look! The English flag!

FATHER: It's from England, all right.

MOTHER: After all these years.

JENNY: Here come the captain and some others.

(*Captain Littlestone, Mr. and Mrs. Wolston, their two daughters and Extra Sailors, if desired, enter from left.*)

CAPTAIN (*shaking hands with Father*): How do you do? I am Captain Littlestone. (*Indicating the others behind him.*) Mr. and Mrs. Wolston and their daughters, Mary and Martha—my passengers.

FATHER: We are the Robinson family—my wife and four sons. . . .

CAPTAIN (*breaking in, as he notices Jenny*): And you must be Jenny Montrose. (*Jenny nods.*) Your father sent us to find you.

JENNY (*happily*): Then he's all right! I'm so grateful for the news.

MR. WOLSTON (*looking around*): Where are we? What is this place?

MOTHER: We call it New Switzerland. It's a pleasant and abundant land.

MRS. WOLSTON (*to Mother*): What healthy sons you have. This must be a wonderful place to live.

MARY (*in delight*): What an adventure this turned out to be!

MARTHA (*excitedly glancing around*): I can hardly wait to scout around. (*Somewhat bashfully to the Robinsons.*) Would one of you be so kind as to take us on a tour? (*All four boys step forward, eagerly ad libbing:* I will . . . Allow me . . . Come along . . . Let's go. *The others chuckle.*)

CAPTAIN: I suggest we get better acquainted before seeing the sights. (*To Robinsons.*) Mr. Wolston hasn't been feeling too well the last several days. Perhaps you folks could put him up for a while.

MOTHER: Of course. Please be our honored guests.

CAPTAIN: My ship is at your disposal. Do you wish to return home as soon as possible? What are your plans?

FATHER: We have already decided what to do in case of rescue. Franz and Fritz will return to Europe. Later, they will come back to visit the rest of us who have decided to remain on New Switzerland.

MR. WOLSTON (*breathing deeply, appreciatively*): The fresh, clean air makes me feel better already. (*To Mrs. Wolston.*) Perhaps we, too, should consider becoming citizens of this fine country.

MRS. WOLSTON: If the Robinsons will let us stay awhile, we can see if the life agrees with us.

MARY (*to Robinsons*): Please, would you let us join you?

MARTHA: We'd be helpful citizens—we promise.

ERNEST: Make yourselves welcome. It's no longer just our island—it belongs to you, too.

CAPTAIN: I suggest we celebrate this happy occasion with a banquet. Our ship has an ample supply of all that we need.

JACK (*eagerly*): And we have a storehouse loaded with fine foods!

JENNY (*with enthusiasm*): Mother Robinson bakes the tastiest cakes ever!

MR. WOLSTON (*rubbing his hands*): On with it! My appetite is restored already.

MRS. WOLSTON: Why don't we build a barbecue pit right here on the shore?

MARTHA (*clapping hands*): How romantic!

MARY (*brightly*): How romantic! (*All engage in task of clear-*

ing the center stage and arranging a barbecue pit with stones and firewood. As they work, Jack separates himself from the others by walking downstage right. He bends over a basket and quickly breaks and examines oysters, throwing the shells over his shoulder. Finally, he jerks upright, stares in amazement at the pearl between his fingers.)

JACK (*shouting jubilantly, holding up the pearl*): Look! Everyone look! (*Racing back to others who silently crowd around him.*) A pearl! Look—at last! A precious pearl! Mother! Jenny! Do you know what this means? Pearl necklaces! For both of you! (*Almost hysterically.*) My first real pearl! (*Others smile, chuckle.*)

MARY (*with wide eyes*): Do you think you can find enough for us, too? (*Sighing dreamily.*) A pearl necklace. Oh. . . .

MARTHA (*eagerly*): I like pearls, too!

JACK (*proudly posing*): From now on please call me the Pearl Prince. (*Pleased with the idea.*) That's a clever title—the Pearl Prince of New Switzerland!

FRANZ (*grinning at Jack*): Yes, Pearl Prince . . . all you need is about three hundred more. (*Gesturing to the ladies.*) Yes, three hundred more ought to make necklaces for our five ladies.

JACK (*frowning, suddenly dismayed, scratching his head*): Just three hundred more?

JENNY (*grinning*): That's all, my proud prince, just three hundred more pearls.

JACK (*dismayed, shocked*): What have I gotten myself into?

MARY (*wagging a finger at Jack*): A promise is a promise.

JACK (*shrugging good-naturedly as the others chuckle*): Oh, well . . . back to work. (*He sadly returns to the basket, sits down, digs into it, resumes breaking open the oysters.*)

FATHER (*gesturing broadly*): This is a great day for New Switzerland! Long may she flourish!

FRITZ: A wonderful day for everyone! On with the celebration! (*Players busily prepare for the banquet. The curtain falls.*)

Don Quixote Saves the Day

CHARACTERS

Narrator	First Guard
Don Quixote	Second Guard
Sancho Panza	First Lady
Roque Guinart	Second Lady
First Bandit	Third Lady
Second Bandit	Fourth Lady
Third Bandit	Extra Bandits
Fourth Bandit	

INTRODUCTION BY NARRATOR

Ladies and gentlemen, tonight we have for you an adventure story that is delightfully different. We believe you will find it amusing. Yes, you might call our drama an adventure in humor . . . a tender kind of humor that warms your heart at the same time that it makes you laugh. Our play is entitled "Don Quixote Saves the Day." It is adapted from the classic story *Don Quixote de la Mancha*, written by Miguel Cervantes.

Perhaps you remember that Don Quixote was a Spanish gentleman who fancied himself a dashing knight-in-armor. Assisted by his squire, Sancho Panza, Don Quixote galloped about the countryside seeking to conquer castles held by wicked men and to rescue fair ladies in distress. I'm afraid the Don wasn't exactly a heroic figure as he sat upon his scrawny horse, but he is at least a sincere, kindly, and intensely interesting adventurer.

Our play opens just after Don Quixote has charged with his horse against an enemy. Perhaps the enemy was a windmill which he mistook for a swinging giant, or maybe it was a flock of sheep that appeared to be an attacking army. But anyway, we shall see what happened to him after his ferocious charge.

SETTING AT RISE OF CURTAIN

The scene takes place along a country road. Bushes and rocks are set in background. A sign with an arrow reads "Barcelona." A large bush stands apart from the others near stage center; however, it should be placed so as to allow room for action at stage center. Sancho Panza is hidden behind the bush, unseen by the audience.

Don Quixote is sprawled motionless in an awkward and comical position at downstage. Stunned, as if spilled from his horse, his arms and legs are flung out from his body. His sword and shield (both cardboard) are scattered about. After remaining motionless for a few seconds he stirs, slowly raises his head.

DON QUIXOTE (*groaning*): I, Don Quixote de la Mancha, spilled to the earth like an acorn in the wind. My enemies have worked their evil black magic against me. Never mind, I shall rise and charge once more. (*Painfully rising, hobbling toward sword, picking it up, shouting defiantly in several directions.*) Ho! Show yourself, cowards! My blade is ready! (*Suddenly groaning loudly, painfully holding his side, sitting on a rock.*) If only my faithful squire were here. (*Thinking.*) Whatever happened to my faithful Sancho Panza? (*Remembering.*) Ah, yes, I appointed him governor of an island.

SANCHO PANZA (*calling from behind the bush*): Help! Who's up there? I need your assistance! (*Note: Panza is trapped in a cave supposedly behind the bush. He remains unseen behind the bush until indicated otherwise in the stage directions.*) DON QUIXOTE (*startled, tilting his head*): That voice! Where have I heard it before?

SANCHO PANZA: I am Sancho Panza, most faithful squire to the gallant Don Quixote de la Mancha. I am trapped down here in a cave. Whoever you are, please come to my rescue.

DON QUIXOTE (*angrily leaping up, waving his sword*): No, no! It can't be! It's the voice of an evil magician! (*Whirling about in an effort to find source of voice, shouting a challenge.*) On guard, evil one! Taste the blade of Don Quixote de la Mancha! (*Suddenly groaning, painfully holding his side, staggering back to the rock.*) The wicked wizard has stabbed me with his curse. Ohhhhh!

SANCHO PANZA (*joyously*): Master! By all that's pure and noble, it's the voice of my master! Don Quixote, attend to the cries of your humble squire. Truly it is I, Sancho Panza!

DON QUIXOTE (*delighted*): My day of good fortune! It is indeed his voice! (*Peering, searching around.*) Sancho Panza, where are you?

SANCHO PANZA: Down here! In the cave behind the bush! (*Quixote confusedly hobbles to two or three of the smaller bushes and calls Panza's name, but gets no reply. Note: To make it appear that Panza is down in a cave, Quixote looks and calls downward. He finally goes to the correct bush.*)

DON QUIXOTE (*calling*): Sancho! Answer me, squire!

SANCHO PANZA (*calling*): Here I am!

DON QUIXOTE (*wagging a reproving finger down at Panza*): Ah, there you are, my foolish rabbit. It's the duty of a squire to assist his master, not the other way round. (*Sighing.*) Ah, well, give me your hand. (*Quixote stretches over and extends a hand.*

113

Panza's hand appears from behind the bush to grasp Quixote's. They struggle for a moment, then instead of Panza coming up, Quixote is pulled, shrieking, behind the bush as if down into the cave. Both ad lib distressed cries from behind the bush, such as: Sancho, you clumsy ox! ... Sorry, sir ... A miserable hole ... Let's try again. *Panza finally crawls into view at the side of the bush. He extends his hand to Quixote, and after another struggling tug, both again fall out of sight. The confused cries are repeated. Finally, both crawl out on opposite sides of the bush, not seeing each other. Both yell downward.*)

SANCHO PANZA (*calling, extending hand*): Grab my hand, master!

DON QUIXOTE (*calling, extending hand*): Sancho, take my hand! (*Both frown in bewilderment.*)

SANCHO PANZA: Master, look up here!

DON QUIXOTE: No, Sancho, you look up here! (*Both look up at sky, shaking heads. They crawl around the bush in the same direction, exchanging sides of the bush. They cannot see each other, of course, because of the bush between them.*)

SANCHO PANZA (*on his knees, calling down*): Noble knight, are you all right? (*As he continues to call, Don Quixote circles around the bush to stand in back of Panza, eyeing him sternly. Not noticing Quixote, Panza again calls.*) Please, sir, give me your hand!

DON QUIXOTE (*angrily raising his hand as if to strike*): I'll give you my hand all right, foolish squire! (*Panza whirls, Quixote holds arm in striking position, both stare, suddenly embrace while ad libbing happy greetings, such as:* Old friend! ... How are you? ... Together again! ... I've missed you!)

DON QUIXOTE (*breaking away, snatching his sword, shouting dramatically*): Enough! Prepare to mount! We must ride on to Barcelona!

SANCHO PANZA (*eagerly*): There is adventure in Barcelona?

DON QUIXOTE (*dramatically, with hand over heart*): The sweetest adventure known to the human heart—the adventure of love. We must ride on to the castle of my fair Lady Dulcinea.

SANCHO PANZA (*spiritlessly, somewhat bored*): Oh, yes, that woman you call Lady Dulcinea.

DON QUIXOTE (*angrily raising his sword*): Say that again, squire—with purity and reverence.

SANCHO PANZA (*shrugging, sighing, holding hand over heart, trying to please Quixote*): Your fair and fragile flower—the Lady Dulcinea.

DON QUIXOTE (*lowering sword, satisfied*): Much better. Now let us find our horses and be off.

(*As they separate to walk toward opposite wings, Roque Guinart and his four bandits appear, three at one wing, two at the other. The bandits, armed with toy pistols and cardboard swords, silently watch as Quixote and Panza approach. Panza sees them, shouts in alarm.*)

SANCHO PANZA (*fearfully*): Master, we're surrounded by bandits!

DON QUIXOTE (*proudly drawing himself up, shaking his sword*): No, indeed, it is I who have surrounded the bandits! (*To Roque, who steps forward.*) Surrender, you prince of scoundrels! Drop your evil weapons before the feet of your royal knight. (*Roque is so surprised that he drops his sword and laughs.*)

ROQUE (*to his men, chuckling*): You heard his command. Drop them! (*The bandits grin, drop their weapons as Roque speaks to Quixote.*) And to whom do we have the honor of surrendering? Your name, sir?

SANCHO PANZA: My master is Don Quixote de la Mancha— the bravest knight in all the kingdom.

DON QUIXOTE (*proudly, hand over heart*): In the service of the fair Lady Dulcinea.

ROQUE (*bowing, grinning*): At your mercy, sir. Pray do not deal harshly with us.

DON QUIXOTE (*frowning at the bandits*): A more miserable band of cutthroats I have not set eyes upon. Who are you—how dare you interfere with my journey?

ROQUE: Sir, I am called Roque Guinart. Some do indeed call us cutthroats and thieves. (*Sighing regretfully.*) Most distasteful titles to be sure, but very true, I'm afraid. (*Bowing.*) I assure, you, however, that I am most respectful to knights in armor such as you. Permit my comrades in crime to introduce themselves. (*Grinning, commanding his men.*) Scoundrels, show your respect!

FIRST BANDIT (*bowing to Quixote*): I am called by many names, most of them quite unkind . . . such as pickpocket, blackmailer, smuggler.

SECOND BANDIT (*gesturing to First Bandit*): Add "highwayman" to all that and you have my identity, sir.

THIRD BANDIT: My speciality is forgery. (*Bowing.*) Sorry, sir.

FOURTH BANDIT: Your prisoner is an all-around no-good. Your honesty makes me ashamed to admit it.

SANCHO PANZA (*wide-eyed and frightened*): Master, I fear we are in undesirable company.

ROQUE (*businesslike*): And now that we understand each other, gentlemen, suppose we get on with our business. (*Gesturing to his men, who seize Panza. Panza struggles, finally gives up.*)

DON QUIXOTE (*angrily shaking his sword at Roque*): Release him at once or I shall run you through! (*Roque grins, again gestures to his men who also seize Quixote. Quixote struggles and screams.*) Villains! Thieves! Unhand me! (*Quixote and Panza are forced to sit on rocks alongside each other. The bandits stand guard over them.*)

ROQUE (*to Quixote*): You see, sir, I am somewhat of a knight of the road myself. However, I lack the gallantry of a champion such as you—I require payment for my services. (*Holding out palm.*) Your purses, please. (*Quixote and Panza leap up but are shoved back. Roque smiles pleasantly.*) I am glad to see that you have regained your self-control. Shall we again discuss the matter of money, that is, your money?

SANCHO PANZA (*pleading*): Of a truth, sir, we haven't a coin between us. Search our pockets if you like.

DON QUIXOTE (*to Panza, somewhat startled*): Are we indeed as poor as all that? (*Panza sadly nods as Quixote speaks proudly to Roque.*) Our only wealth is honor and honesty.

SANCHO PANZA: We are also rich in pride. (*Muttering to himself.*) Oh, for less pride and more money.

DON QUIXOTE (*reproving Panza*): Silence! You tarnish the noble profession of knighthood with your greed.

FIRST BANDIT (*cupping an ear toward left wing*): Listen! I hear an approaching carriage. (*Grinning.*) Perhaps our new guests have heavier purses.

ROQUE (*nodding*): Ah! Suppose you give them our customary

greeting. (*The first three bandits snatch up their weapons and vanish into left wing. The Fourth Bandit remains on guard over Quixote and Panza.*)

FOURTH BANDIT (*to Quixote and Panza*): Where are you bound for, noble knight and faithful squire?

DON QUIXOTE (*bewildered*): Bless me, but I've quite forgotten.

SANCHO PANZA (*sadly*): We rarely know where we are going.

DON QUIXOTE (*to Roque*): Turn into an honest man, sir, and I shall ride with you upon your adventures . . . or rather, I shall permit you to ride with me. (*Rising.*) Come, Sancho, we must find our horses. (*Roque and the Fourth Bandit shrug and let them go.*) I hope my fiery steed has not wandered too far. (*Hobbling toward right, calling.*) Rosinante, where are you? Rosinante! (*Quixote and Panza exit at right.*)

ROQUE (*staring after them in amused disbelief*): Do my eyes deceive me or have we just witnessed an amazing fellow who calls himself Don Quixote de la Mancha? (*Shrugging, then briskly rubbing his palms together as he looks toward left.*) Ah, our guests have arrived! (*The four ladies and their two guards are escorted onstage by the three bandits.*)

FIRST BANDIT (*with exaggerated courtesy to the captives*): Here you are, ladies and gentlemen, safe in the camp of Roque Guinart and his comrades. (*To Roque.*) Please meet our captives —I mean our guests.

FIRST GUARD (*angrily*): When word of this reaches the governor he'll have your heads!

SECOND BANDIT: Come now, no need to be upset. (*To Third Bandit.*) Show our guests how considerate we are.

THIRD BANDIT: Ah, yes, we must extend our usual courtesies. For example, we must relieve our weary travellers of their weighty baggage. (*Holding up forefinger.*) I'll show you what I mean. (*Snatching money bags from the guards, he weighs them in his palm, grinning*.) See! We relieve you of all your unnecessary weight! (*The bandits laugh. The Third Bandit steps behind the First Lady, fingers the back of her necklace while smiling.*) Surely I should offer you the same courtesy.

FIRST LADY (*slapping in back of her*): Insolent thief!

SECOND LADY (*indignantly, to guards*): Don't just tremble like frightened rabbits . . . do something.

SECOND GUARD (*miserably*): What would you have me do, my lady?

THIRD LADY (*gesturing*): Uh . . . whatever you're supposed to do . . . slap their faces, pull their hair . . . do anything.

FOURTH LADY: After all, guards are supposed to guard. Start guarding us!

ROQUE (*laughing, handing a sword to Second Guard*): The ladies are perfectly right. You must strike in their behalf. (*The guard miserably eyes the sword.*) Come, man, protect your fair ladies!

SECOND GUARD (*weakly*): Yes, sir. (*He looks sadly around, slowly and spiritlessly raises the sword, groans, almost weeps, drops sword to ground. The bandits roar with merriment.*)

ROQUE (*approaching ladies*): Sorry, ladies, but we must earn our daily bread. (*Holding out palm.*) May I?

FIRST LADY (*indignantly drawing herself up*): You may not. Take my jewels and I shall scream. (*Nodding.*) Quite loudly.

FOURTH BANDIT (*sighing dreamily*): Ah . . . it's been weeks since I heard the delightful scream from a fair throat. Like music it is. (*Wagging finger to First Lady as he steps up to her.*) Don't forget your promise—a piercing, full-throated unladylike scream. (*To other ladies.*) Perhaps you will join her—make it a harmonious chorus! (*Bandits chuckle.*)

SECOND LADY (*nodding primly to other ladies*): We shall scream indeed! Perhaps a fearless champion will ride to our rescue.

ROQUE (*grinning, snapping fingers as he glances toward right wing*): A champion, you say? I think it quite likely your prayers may be answered. (*Eyeing necklace of any lady.*) Such a lovely lady has no need for this ornament. (*The ladies scream, race toward right, scream again as the bandits follow.*)

DON QUIXOTE (*racing furiously onstage from right, shaking his sword*): Don Quixote to the rescue! (*He trips, sprawls awkwardly, sword flying. Panza races in, gently picks him up.*)

SANCHO PANZA: Easy, master.

DON QUIXOTE (*pushing Panza away, glancing angrily around*): What contemptible betrayal is this? (*To Roque.*) I warn you, sir! Release these fair flowers of womanhood at once! At once, sir, or you'll answer to the sword of Don Quixote de la Mancha!

SANCHO PANZA (*tugging at Quixote's coat:*) Master . . . please.

FIRST BANDIT (*amusing himself with Quixote*): You don't understand, fearless one. We are merely relieving the burdens from our weary guests. Surely we must be good hosts to them.

DON QUIXOTE (*taken in by the double talk, relieved*): Well, now, that is worthy enough. (*Peering closely at faces of ladies.*) Do I see the fair face of the Lady Dulcinea among you? (*Brightly.*) Ah, yes . . . my heart bows to you. (*Bowing to First Lady.*) My fondest affection, Lady Dulcinea. (*Bowing to Second Lady.*) My heart melts before you. (*Bowing to Third Lady.*) Lady Dulcinea, I love you as always. (*Bowing to Fourth Lady.*) I ask only your tender smile, fair one. (*The ladies exchange puzzled glances.*)

SANCHO PANZA (*explaining with embarrassment*): To my master, all ladies are his fair Lady Dulcinea.

THIRD LADY (*in confusion as she gestures toward Quixote*): This . . . this is our fearless champion? Dear me.

ROQUE (*placing a kindly hand on Quixote's shoulder*): Perhaps he's not the dashing knight you wish for, ladies, but I assure you he is nevertheless a fine friend. (*Shrugging.*) As a matter of fact, I am inclined to let you go for his sake.

SECOND BANDIT (*protesting*): But the jewels . . . we've rightly earned them.

ROQUE (*quietly*): Perhaps Don Quixote has also earned our guests the right to keep them. (*To bandits.*) Stand back, comrades. (*The bandits shrug and retreat from the ladies.*)

FOURTH LADY (*to Roque, gratefully*): You have a spark of goodness after all. Thank you.

THIRD BANDIT (*to ladies, while gesturing toward Quixote*): You had best thank Don Quixote de la Mancha who has softened five of the hardest hearts in the land.

FOURTH BANDIT: It's not often that we give mercy in place of the sword.

FIRST BANDIT (*to ladies and guards*): Come along before we change our minds. I'll escort you to your carriage.

FIRST LADY (*to other ladies*): First we must pay our debt. (*Stepping before Don Quixote, with bow or curtsy*): Your Lady Dulcinea thanks you.

SECOND LADY (*doing likewise*): Bless you. Truly you are a noble knight.

THIRD LADY (*doing likewise*): Your Lady Dulcinea shall remember your kindness forever. (*The Fourth Lady also bows, then kisses her fingertips, touches them tenderly on Quixote's cheek. Quixote almost weeps at their spontaneous show of affection for him. As the ladies, guards, and the First Bandit exit at left, he raises a limp and weary hand in farewell.*)

ROQUE (*beckoning to Panza who approaches, speaking quietly*): Help your master to his horse. (*Placing a friendly hand on Panza's shoulder.*) Take good care of him. (*Nodding at the still-stunned Quixote whose hand is still upraised.*) Take very good care.

SANCHO PANZA (*gently taking Quixote's elbow*): Come, sir,

Lady Dulcinea awaits your arrival in Barcelona. (*Panza leads the dazed Quixote a few steps toward the right. Quixote pauses, slowly raises his fingers to touch the spot where his cheek was kissed.*)

DON QUIXOTE (*a pathetic but sympathetic figure, he whispers in wonderment as he stares outward*): Did you see, Sancho? . . . did you see my Lady Dulcinea? (*Looking at his fingers.*) She kissed my cheek. My lady kissed my cheek.

SANCHO PANZA (*tenderly, emotionally*): Yes, master . . . she kissed you. Your lady truly loves you. She will always love you. Come. . . . (*Panza slowly leads the weary Quixote offstage. The bandits, who are quieted and humbled by the emotional experience, gaze after them as Roque speaks.*)

ROQUE (*also gazing, speaking soberly, philosophically*): A foolish man, Don Quixote de la Mancha? Perhaps. But also a sincere soul who does the best he knows how. A blundering, awkward clown? Yes, but also a human being who yearns desperately to be loved. That, I suppose, is all that the rest of us really want—just to be loved by someone. Perhaps, my friends, if a man is loved enough he will be a good man . . . which is all that really matters. What difference does it make if a man is foolish or clumsy? . . . as long as he is a good man. (*After gazing toward the right wing a moment longer, Roque gestures to his men. All quietly and soberly exit at left. The curtain falls.*)

The
—End—